COLLEGE GEOMETRY

THE APPLETON-CENTURY MATHEMATICS SERIES

Edited by Raymond W. Brink

Intermediate Algebra, Second Edition
by Raymond W. Brink

College Algebra, Second Edition
by Raymond W. Brink

Algebra—College Course, Second Edition
by Raymond W. Brink

A First Year of College Mathematics, Second Edition
by Raymond W. Brink

Calculus
by Lloyd L. Smail

Analytic Geometry and Calculus
by Lloyd L. Smail

College Geometry
by Leslie H. Miller

Solid Analytic Geometry
by John M. H. Olmsted

Intermediate Analysis
by John M. H. Olmsted

The Mathematics of Finance
by Franklin C. Smith

Plane Trigonometry, Revised Edition
by Raymond W. Brink

Spherical Trigonometry
by Raymond W. Brink

Analytic Geometry, Revised Edition
by Raymond W. Brink

Essentials of Analytic Geometry
by Raymond W. Brink

COLLEGE GEOMETRY

by
Leslie H. Miller

ASSOCIATE PROFESSOR OF MATHEMATICS
THE OHIO STATE UNIVERSITY

NEW YORK: APPLETON-CENTURY-CROFTS, INC.

Copyright, © 1957 by

APPLETON-CENTURY-CROFTS, INC.

517–1

Library of Congress Card Number: 57–5574

PRINTED IN THE UNITED STATES OF AMERICA

PREFACE

Primarily this book contains a synthetic development of advanced Euclidean geometry. The text grew out of mimeographed notes used in classes containing both prospective mathematics teachers and liberal arts students.

The book attempts to encourage constructive reasoning by stressing generalizations, alternate solutions, and related problems. Numerous discussions serve to motivate new work and to suggest further extensions.

The first six chapters form the basis for a brief course. A richer and more extensive course is obtained by including a selection of material from the remaining chapters, which are largely independent. Geometric constructions are stressed, since many students enjoy constructions and show interest in finding unusual solutions, discussing special cases, and proposing generalizations. The solution of advanced construction problems requires the introduction of generalized theorems.

Considerable elementary geometry appears in the first four chapters to provide a review as well as illustrative material for the discussion of fundamental concepts.

Geometric transformations are stressed in Chapters 5, 6, and 7. Chapter 5 discusses several elementary transformations. In Chapter 6, inversion is discussed and is used to solve the problem of Apollonius, while Chapter 7 is devoted to certain properties of the projective transformation. Chapter 8 includes a discussion of special points and circles associated with a triangle.

Chapters 9, 10, and 11 develop selected topics not usually found in a text of this type; an instructor may decide to assign portions of these chapters for special reports rather than to use them as parts of the basic course. Chapter 12 discusses famous problems of ancient geometry whose solutions cannot be constructed by ruler and compass.

In addition to the exercises at the end of each section, there is a set of review exercises for each of the first nine chapters. Some of these exercises are marked by stars to indicate that solutions may require information not given in the text.

The author is grateful for suggestions made by several colleagues and by numerous students. He deeply appreciates the helpful editorial comments of Professor R. W. Brink.

Columbus, Ohio

L. H. M.

CONTENTS

CONTENTS

Chapter 4

GEOMETRIC LOCI

Chapter 5

ELEMENTARY TRANSFORMATIONS

Chapter 6

INVERSION

Chapter 7

PROJECTIVE PROPERTIES

Chapter 8

PROPERTIES OF CIRCLES AND TRIANGLES

Chapter 9

A PROBLEM OF STEINER

Chapter 10

GENERALIZATION OF A QUADRILATERAL
CONSTRUCTION PROBLEM

Chapter 11

CONCURRENT LINES ASSOCIATED WITH A TRIANGLE

Chapter 12

IMPOSSIBLE RULER AND COMPASS CONSTRUCTIONS

COLLEGE GEOMETRY

1

Review

<hr/>

1.1 INTRODUCTORY REMARKS

The first four chapters of this book contain a review of material found in a secondary school course in plane geometry. The review material is, however, interspersed with related new material. Construction problems are used both to review elementary theorems and to motivate the introduction of more general theorems. Students are encouraged to solve construction problems by alternate methods, to investigate special cases, and to attempt to formulate and solve more general problems.

A *theorem* consists of two parts: the *hypothesis*, a statement of what is given; and the *conclusion*, a statement of what must be true whenever the hypothesis is true. The *proof* of a theorem is a demonstration that the conclusion is true whenever the hypothesis is true. Information not contained in the hypothesis is often needed in the proof of a theorem; such information may include other theorems, postulates, or definitions. This means that at any stage in the development of plane geometry a precise knowledge of earlier work is essential.

A discussion of plane geometry usually starts with the implied assumption that students are familiar with elementary laws of logic. It is clearly impossible to define every term used since, for example, the first term defined would require use of terms not yet defined. Among the undefined terms of geometry are *point*, *line*, and *plane*. Other terms, such as *perimeter*, *pi*, *perpendicular*, and *pentagon*, are assigned meanings by *definitions*.

Certain statements, called *postulates* or *axioms*, are assumed to be true, without proof, for the particular geometrical system under study. The character of a mathematical system is largely determined by the postulates that are chosen. Postulates may provide information about undefined terms, as in the statement that two points determine a line.

In any mathematical system, postulates are indispensable; they provide a starting place for logical development.

Because of the importance of proofs, postulates, and definitions, these topics will be discussed in more detail in following sections where illustrations from elementary geometry will be considered.

EXERCISES

1. In a logical development of geometry must every technical word be defined?

2. Is it true that the postulates of geometry need no proof because they are obviously true?

3. Consider the theorem "If two straight lines intersect, the vertical angles are equal." State the hypothesis and the conclusion. Prove the theorem. List all axioms and definitions used in the proof.

4. Consider the theorem "A quadrilateral is a parallelogram if the opposite sides are equal." What is the hypothesis? What is the conclusion? Prove the theorem.

1.2 THE SPIRIT OF GEOMETRY

There are rather obvious practical applications for many of the theorems of plane geometry. The present discussion is not primarily concerned with applications but is more interested in the spirit of inquiry typified by questions such as "How was it done?" or "Why was this considered?" or "How is this related to other topics?" or "Can this method be extended to other problems?" The student of mathematics should not be content simply to master the proof of an assigned theorem; in addition he should seek to relate the theorem to past and to future work.

As an example, consider the elementary theorem "The area of a triangle is one-half the product of the base and the altitude." This can be a starting point for an intensive review of secondary school geometry. The adequately prepared student will be able to trace the main steps needed to prove this theorem. He might relate this theorem to another concerning the area of a parallelogram and to a definition of the area of a rectangle. He will realize that the theorem under discussion must be preceded by a discussion of measurements of lengths and areas, by numerous definitions, and by theorems concerning properties of congruent triangles. He may consider various extensions, such as using the theorem for the area of a triangle, combined with a limiting process, to derive a formula for the area of a circle. He might consider an analogous theorem in three dimensions and trace the main steps needed to establish a theorem concerning the volume of a tetrahedron.

EXERCISES

1. Give definitions for the words *triangle* and *tetrahedron*. Mention one way in which a tetrahedron may be considered as analogous to a triangle.

2. Sometimes the area of a triangle is defined as the portion of a plane bounded by the sides of the triangle; more often area is defined as a number associated with a triangle. How can both definitions be correct?

3. Is the statement "The area of a rectangle is the product of the base and the altitude" a definition, a theorem, or a postulate? Might it logically be a theorem in one text and a definition in a second text?

4. If two geometric figures are congruent, they have equal areas. Do you consider this statement to be a theorem, a postulate, or a definition?

5. Prove that the diagonals of a parallelogram bisect each other. Specifically point out where you used a definition, a theorem, and a postulate in your proof.

1.3 DEFINITIONS

A critical student may note that the exercises at the end of sections 1.1 and 1.2 (§§ 1.1 and 1.2) involve definitions, postulates, and theorems, which are topics not yet considered in detail. These exercises were included at these places with the hope that a discussion would indicate that a more detailed study is appropriate.

In the development of a system of geometry, it is necessary to know what terms are taken as undefined; a precise definition is needed for each other technical expression. A *definition* is an agreement concerning the use of a word, symbol, or expression; it must give a meaning of the thing defined in terms of something which has either been defined earlier or has been taken as undefined.

It is not feasible to give a complete list of all definitions to be used in geometry in section I of a text and then follow with a list of all postulates in section II. Some definitions depend on postulates, whereas some postulates contain defined terms. For example, the definition of *parallel lines* as lines in the same plane which do not intersect depends on the postulate that a line is unlimited in extent. This is one reason for introducing definitions as needed.

Before defining a new term, it may be necessary to make decisions about the properties which the term is to imply. Which of the three configurations in Figure 1 can properly be called quadrilaterals depends upon the definition of the word *quadrilateral*. If a person tries to simplify the task of defining a quadrilateral by excluding configurations like *EFGH* and *IJKL* in Figure 1, he still must decide whether or not his definition of a quadrilateral should include mention of sides, vertices, area, diagonals, interior angles, etc. This example is given to point out that a general idea about the meaning of a mathematical term may be insufficient. In reading a text, the student must accept a definition given by the author, even when he considers an alternate definition to be better.

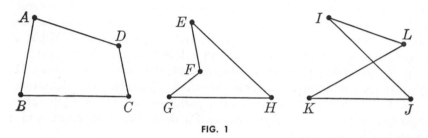

FIG. 1

A *simple polygon* is a figure in a plane, composed of a fixed number of points, called *vertices*, and the same number of line segments, called *sides*, which connect the vertices in order. In a *simple convex polygon*, two sides cannot intersect at a point other than a vertex, and no interior angle can be larger than a straight angle. In this book, the word *polygon* is used to designate a simple convex polygon, unless stated otherwise. A polygon with three sides is a *triangle;* one with four sides is a *quadrilateral;* and one with five sides is a *pentagon.*

With the above definitions, the word *quadrilateral* applies to *ABCD*, in Figure 1, but not to *EFGH* or to *IJKL*. (These figures may be called a *concave* quadrilateral and a *re-entrant* quadrilateral, respectively.)

There is general agreement as to what configuration should be called a parallelogram. Since the important function of a definition is to characterize completely the quantity defined, either of two different definitions may be acceptable. In this book, a *parallelogram* is defined as a quadrilateral having opposite sides parallel. An alternate definition might call a parallelogram a quadrilateral having opposite sides equal. A third possible definition states that if two sides are both equal and parallel, then a quadrilateral is a parallelogram. When one of these definitions is chosen, the remaining two statements become theorems to be proved.

The topic of definitions, in common with most topics in mathematics, cannot be covered in one short lesson. As a person's experience and knowledge increases, it may become desirable to modify or to extend previous definitions. In future work, for example, a more general definition of a quadrilateral will be introduced. At present it is suggested that a student should review critically his knowledge of the following terms; he should be able to define correctly, use, illustrate, and spell each word. The statement "I know what the word means but I can't define it" is not acceptable.

acute	diagonal	pi
adjacent angles	diameter	polygon
altitude	equal	radius
arc	equilateral	regular polygon
bisector	exterior angle	quadrilateral
center	hexagon	rectangle
central angle	hypotenuse	right angle
chord	hypothesis	secant
circle	inscribed angle	square
circumference	isosceles	straight angle
collinear	median	supplement
complement	obtuse	tangent
concentric	octagon	transversal
concurrent	parallel lines	trisect
congruent	parallelogram	vertex
converse	pentagon	vertical angles
decagon	perpendicular	

EXERCISES

1. Look up definitions for the words *definition, axiom, theorem,* and *proof,* using a standard dictionary. Would you call the definitions precise?

2. Can a dictionary be used to find satisfactory mathematical definitions for the words *centroid, collinear, complement, congruent,* and *converse?*

3. Is a parallelogram also a trapezoid? Support your answer by quoting definitions.

4. Discuss both the possibility and the desirability of defining a parallelogram as a quadrilateral in which both pairs of opposite sides are equal and parallel.

5. Why would the following definition be unsatisfactory? A quadrilateral consists of four lines and the four points in which these lines intersect.

1.4 POSTULATES

The words *axiom* and *postulate* are both used to mean something which is assumed to be true as a basis for the development of a mathematical system. Examples of common axioms and postulates of *Euclidean* plane geometry are given below.

  a. A quantity may be substituted for its equal.
  b. Quantities equal to the same quantity, or to equal quantities, are equal to each other.
  c. The whole of a quantity is equal to the sum of its parts.
  d. If equals are added to equals, the sums are equal.
  e. If equals are subtracted from equals, the differences are equal.
  f. If equals are multiplied by equals, the products are equal.
  g. If equals are divided by equals, not zero, the quotients are equal.
  h. Of two quantities of the same kind, the first is greater than, equal to, or less than the second.
  i. If a first quantity is greater than a second and if the second is greater than a third, the first is greater than the third.
  j. Through every point pass an unlimited number of lines, and on every line are an unlimited number of points.
  k. One and only one line is determined by two points.
  l. Two lines which are not parallel intersect in one and only one point.
  m. A geometric figure may be moved without changing its size or shape.
  n. A circle may be drawn using any point as center and any length as radius.
  o. Circles with equal radii are equal.
  p. A line cannot intersect a circle in more than two points.
  q. All straight angles are equal.
  r. All right angles are equal.
  s. At a point on a line one, and only one, perpendicular to the line can be drawn.
  t. Through a given point one, and only one, line can be drawn parallel to the given line.
  u. A line segment has one, and only one, midpoint.

The postulates given above are representative but do not make up a complete set of all the postulates of Euclidean geometry. A complete set of postulates must be *consistent*, so no two contradictory statements can be derived using the postulates. Ideally a set of postulates should be *independent*, so no postulate can be proved true using the remaining postulates. Proving independence can be extremely difficult, even for a small set of postulates.

The postulates of a mathematical system determine what theorems can be proved and the development of such a system then becomes a search for previously undiscovered "truths." Mathematics never absolutely guarantees that a statement about space relations is true or false, but only that if certain postulates are true then other statements must also be true. There are different types of geometry corresponding to different sets of postulates. *Euclidean* geometry is the familiar system based on the postulates contained in Euclid's *Elements*. The realization that other sets of postulates were not only logically possible but that they could have practical applications in explaining observations in physical space was an important step in scientific progress. The Einstein theory of relativity uses a postulate system different from the Euclidean one.

In *projective* geometry, a fundamental postulate states that any two distinct lines in a plane intersect in exactly one point. Theorems proved in projective geometry may be employed by an engineer in designing an airplane wing, or by a painter in finding a vanishing point where parallel lines seem to merge.

EXERCISES

1. Can a postulate be false?

2. Do you suppose that every axiom used in developing the real number system is also an axiom of Euclidean geometry?

3. List several axioms concerning arithmetic operations with unequal quantities and illustrate by numerical examples.

4. What are similarities and differences between the postulates in a mathematical system and the "laws" in a physical science?

5. Do analogies to undefined terms and postulates exist in social sciences?

6. Is it possible to prove contradictory theorems by starting with two different postulate systems? Might this suggest a reason for arguments about topics involving politics or religion?

1.5 SYNTHETIC PROOFS

The usual proof in geometry starts with a statement of the hypothesis and demonstrates that the conclusion must be true by a series of statements each substantiated by a suitable authority. This type of proof, called a *synthetic* proof, is often arranged in a formal manner which may contain some or all of the components listed below.

a. *Theorem:* A general statement of the theorem.
b. *Figure:* A diagram with important features such as points, lines, and angles, identified by letters or symbols.
c. *Given:* A statement of the hypothesis in terms of the letters or symbols of the figure.

   d. To prove: A statement of the conclusion in terms of the figure.

   e. Analysis: A discussion of a plan to be followed in assembling individual steps in the proof.

   f. Proof: A succession of statements, starting with the hypothesis and ending with the conclusion, with the truth of each statement supported by reference to a previous theorem, postulate, or definition.

Exercise 3 of § 1.1 asked for a proof of the theorem used below to illustrate the synthetic method of proof. It is suggested that a student compare his proof with the one presented now.

Theorem 1. *If two lines intersect, the vertical angles are equal.*

Given: In Figure 2, AB and CD are given lines which intersect at point O.

To prove: $\angle AOC = \angle BOD$.

Analysis: Use the fact that $\angle AOC + \angle COB$ is a straight angle equal to straight angle $\angle COB + \angle BOD$.

Proof: 1. Lines AB and CD intersect at O, forming the vertical angles AOC and BOD. This follows from the hypothesis and the definition of vertical angles.

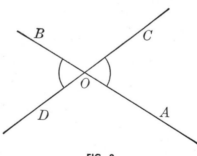

FIG. 2

   2. $\angle AOC + \angle COB$ is a straight angle and $\angle COB + \angle BOD$ is also a straight angle. This is true from the definition of a straight angle.

   3. $\angle AOC + \angle COB = \angle COB + \angle BOD$. The equality follows from the postulate (q of § 1.4) that all straight angles are equal.

   4. $\angle AOC = \angle BOD$. This statement, which completes the proof, is obtained by subtracting equals from equals (Postulate e, § 1.4).

A student should feel free to ask questions (or make suggestions) about a proof presented by someone else. Questions which may be asked about the above proof include: "Is it also necessary to prove that angles BOC and DOA are equal?" or "Step 4 seems to involve subtracting one angle from another; how is this done?" or "Is it possible to prove this theorem without first clearly defining the meaning of equal angles?"

The word *equal* needs special attention, since it may have two distinct interpretations when used in connection with geometric figures. If two angles are equal, it is possible to make the angles exactly coincide (apply Postulate *m* of § 1.4 to move one), and also the number of degrees in one angle is equal to the number of degrees in the other angle. In the statement that a central angle of a circle is equal to its intercepted arc, it is clearly impossible to make the angle and the arc coincide; in this case the equality means that the number of degrees in the arc is equal to the number of degrees in the angle.

In this book every equation involving geometric quantities is considered as a relation between numbers; a second interpretation is permitted, however, when all quantities are of the same kind.

In assigning numbers to geometric quantities, it is necessary to choose units to be used in measuring lengths of line segments, sizes of angles, magnitudes of circular arcs, areas of polygons, etc. The common unit of angular measure is one degree (1°) chosen so that a straight angle contains 180°. The corresponding unit for measuring a circular arc is one degree of arc, chosen so that the entire circumference of a circle contains 360 degrees. The measure in degrees of an angle (or arc) is then a real number which shows how many of the units are contained in the angle (or arc).

A number of useful theorems of elementary geometry contain equalities relating the magnitude of the angle between two intersecting lines with the magnitudes of the arcs which the lines intercept on a circle. For the special case in which the lines pass through the center of the circle, the discussion of the above paragraph leads to the following definition.

Definition 1. *A central angle is measured by its intercepted arc.*

This definition means that the number of degrees in the angle is equal to the number of degrees in the intercepted arc. The equality also holds if both the angle and the arc are measured in other comparable units, such as radians.

Theorem 2. *An exterior angle of a triangle is equal to the sum of the opposite interior angles.*

The proof of Theorem 2 is left as an exercise for the student. The equality may be interpreted either as an equality between numbers or as meaning that two angles can be made to coincide. (The latter case assumes that a method for adding angles is known.)

Theorem 3. *An inscribed angle is measured by one-half of its intercepted arc.*

The proof of Theorem 3 is also left as an exercise for the student, with the hint that Theorem 2 and Definition 1 may be used. It may help first to prove the theorem for the special case in which one side of the angle passes through the center of the circle.

Theorem 4. *An angle formed by two chords intersecting within a circle is measured by one-half the sum of the intercepted arcs.*

A formal synthetic proof will be given for Theorem 4.

Given: The circle O, Figure 3, in which chords AB and CD intersect at point P.

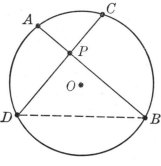

FIG. 3

To prove: $\angle APD = \frac{1}{2}(\widehat{AD} + \widehat{BC})$.

Proof:

STATEMENT	REASON
1. Draw BD.	1. Postulate k, § 1.4.
2. $\angle APD = \angle ABD + \angle BDC$.	2. Theorem 2.
3. $\angle ABD = \frac{1}{2}\widehat{AD}$, and $\angle BDC = \frac{1}{2}\widehat{BC}$.	3. Theorem 3.
4. $\angle APD = \frac{1}{2}(\widehat{AD} + \widehat{BC})$.	4. Axiom a, § 1.4.

EXERCISES

1. In addition to a degree, other units used in measuring angles are minute, second, radian, and mil. Define each of these terms.

2. Explain how Theorem 3 is a limiting case of Theorem 4.

3. Find a numerical relation connecting an interior angle of a triangle and the sum of the two opposite exterior angles.

4. Prove that angles with equal supplements are equal.

5. Prove that two triangles are congruent if two sides and the included angle of one are equal, respectively, to two sides and the included angle of the other.

6. Two congruent triangles have equal areas. What is the converse of this statement? Is the converse a true statement?

1.6 METHODS OF PROOF

The synthetic method of proof is characterized by the process of starting with the hypothesis and working toward the conclusion. In another method, called *analytic,* this process is reversed. The proof begins with the conclusion, which is first shown to be true if some intermediate statement is true; it then leads back to the hypothesis by successive steps. If H represents the hypothesis and C the conclusion of a theorem, an analytic proof takes the form: conclusion C must be true if statement S is true, statement S must be true if the hypothesis H is true; since H is assumed true, the validity of S and of C is established. The analytic method is illustrated by a second proof of Theorem 1 of § 1.5.

Theorem 1 (Analytic Proof). *If two lines intersect, the vertical angles are equal.*

Proof: In Figure 2, where lines AB and CD intersect at point O, it is to be shown that $\angle AOC = \angle BOD$.

1. Angles AOC and BOD must be equal if

$$\angle AOC + \angle BOC = \angle BOD + \angle BOC \quad \text{(Axiom } e, \S 1.4).$$

2. $\angle AOC + \angle BOC = \angle BOD + \angle BOC$ if both ($\angle AOC + \angle BOC$) and ($\angle BOD + \angle BOC$) are straight angles (Postulate q, § 1.4).

3. Both ($\angle AOC + \angle BOC$) and ($\angle BOD + \angle BOC$) are straight angles if AB and CD are straight lines intersecting at O (definition of straight angle).

4. AB and CD are straight lines intersecting at point O (hypothesis).

From step 4, the conclusion of Theorem 1 is established by retracing steps 3, 2, and 1.

Sometimes a distinction is made between a *direct* and an *indirect* method of proof. If a statement is known to be either true or false, it may be proved true, indirectly, by demonstrating that it cannot be false. Theorem 1 is proved once more, this time by an indirect method.

Theorem 1 (Indirect Proof). *If two lines intersect, the vertical angles are equal.*

Proof: In Figure 2, where lines AB and CD intersect at point O, it is to be shown that $\angle AOC = \angle BOD$.

1. Assume that if two lines intersect, the vertical angles are not necessarily equal and that, in Figure 2, $\angle AOC \neq \angle BOD$.

2. From the axiom "If equals are added to unequals, the sums are unequal," it follows that

$$(\angle AOC + \angle BOC) \neq (\angle BOD + \angle BOC).$$

3. By definition, both $(\angle AOC + \angle BOC)$ and $(\angle BOD + \angle BOC)$ are straight angles.

4. From axiom q of § 1.4, it is evident that

$$(\angle AOC + \angle BOC) = (\angle BOD + \angle BOC).$$

The statements in steps 2 and 4 contradict each other; the statement in step 4 is known to be true. Since step 2 follows logically from step 1, the assumption in step 1 is false and the conclusion of the theorem is established.

Methods used in geometry have analogies in many situations that do not involve mathematics in the usual sense. A cook expects a recipe to be arranged in the synthetic, step by step, manner; the person who originated the recipe probably used an analytic approach to decide what ingredients to use; the recipe may have been tested by the indirect method of trying variations to see if they produced better results.

If fifteen children attend a birthday party, someone will, perhaps, discover that two of the children have birthdays during the same month. The general observation "In every group of thirteen or more persons, at least two will have birthdays in the same month" cannot be verified by the direct method of obtaining birth dates for every possible group. It can, however, be proved indirectly by assuming that there is at least one group of thirteen or more persons with no two having birthdays in the same month. This leads to the conclusion that there are thirteen or more months in one year.

The analytic method discussed in this section is not to be confused with *analytic geometry* where, through the introduction of a co-ordinate system, the solution of geometric problems may be reduced to algebraic manipulations. Co-ordinate systems will not be used directly in this book but will be mentioned in some optional exercises. The ease with which analytic geometry may be applied to a wide variety of geometric problems may, in part, explain why synthetic geometry is omitted from the mathematics program of most college students.

EXERCISES

1. Prove that the diagonals of a parallelogram bisect each other.

2. Discuss the logic of an alibi.

3. Use the indirect method to prove that two lines, each parallel to a third line, are parallel to each other.

4. A single counterexample is sufficient to prove that a theorem is not correct. Discuss the truth of the statement that no prime integer is divisible by 2.

5. Is the following theorem true or false? Two triangles are congruent if two sides and an angle of one are equal to the corresponding sides and angle of the other.

1.7 THE CONVERSE OF A THEOREM

If two theorems are related so that either is obtained by interchanging the hypothesis and the conclusion of the other, each theorem is called the *converse* of the other. For example, the converse of "In an isosceles triangle, two angles are equal" is "If two angles of a triangle are equal, the triangle is isosceles." Sometimes, when it is desirable to combine a theorem and its converse into one statement, one of the following forms is used: "A triangle is isosceles if two angles are equal, and *conversely*" or "A triangle is isosceles *if and only if* two angles are equal" or "A *necessary and sufficient condition* for a triangle to be isosceles is that two angles be equal."

Often an error is made by assuming that a statement is true because its converse is known to be true. Although each angle in a square is a right angle, it does not follow that a quadrilateral is a square if each angle is a right angle. Whenever a theorem is proved true, we may attempt to enlarge our mathematical knowledge by investigating the converse. To prove that a general statement is not valid, it is sufficient to find one example for which the statement is not true; we show that a quadrilateral containing four right angles is not necessarily a square by exhibiting a rectangle in which the adjacent sides are unequal. In proving that the converse of a particular theorem is true, the indirect method of proof is often employed.

Theorem 1. *A line parallel to one side of a triangle and cutting the other two sides divides these sides into proportional segments.*

A proof of this theorem may be found in an elementary text. Theorem 2, which is the converse of Theorem 1, will be proved in an indirect manner.

Theorem 2. *A line which divides two sides of a triangle into proportional segments is parallel to the third side.*

Given: In triangle ABC, Figure 4, $\dfrac{AE}{EB} = \dfrac{AD}{DC}$.

To prove: Lines ED and BC are parallel.

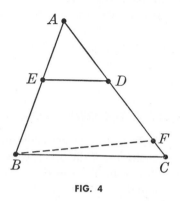

FIG. 4

Analysis: Through B construct a line parallel to ED, cutting AC at F. Show that F and C coincide.

Proof: 1. Assume that ED and BC are not parallel. Through B construct a line parallel to line ED cutting AC at F, with $DF \neq DC$ (Postulate t, § 1.4).

2. In triangle ABF, $\dfrac{AE}{EB} = \dfrac{AD}{DF}$ (Theorem 1).

3. Also $\dfrac{AE}{EB} = \dfrac{AD}{DC}$ (hypothesis).

4. From steps 2 and 3, it follows that $\dfrac{AD}{DC} = \dfrac{AD}{DF}$ (Axiom b, § 1.4).

5. Multiply each side of the equality in step 4 by DC, then multiply by DF, then divide by AD to obtain $DF = DC$ (Axioms f and g, § 1.4).

6. The contradictory statements in steps 1 and 5 show that the assumption in 1 is not correct; therefore, lines ED and BC are parallel.

The following theorem has numerous applications throughout this book. The proof given is typical of the informal style that is used in later work.

Theorem 3. *If two chords intersect within a circle, the product of the segments of one chord is equal to the product of the segments of the other.*

Proof: In Figure 5, chords AB and CD intersect at point P and it is to be shown that $AP \cdot PB = DP \cdot PC$. This is an equality between

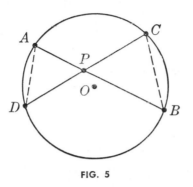

FIG. 5

real numbers since, for example, the symbol AP represents numerically the length of the line segment AP.

The relation to be proved can be expressed in the equivalent form $AP/PD = CP/PB$. Since this proportion suggests the use of similar triangles, lines AD and CB are constructed. Triangles APD and CPB must be similar, with AP corresponding to CP and with PD corresponding to PB, if $\angle ADC = \angle ABC$ and if $\angle BAD = \angle BCD$. The equality of these angles follows from Theorem 3 of § 1.5.

The student is urged to write a statement of the converse of Theorem 3 and then to compare his statement with Theorem 3 of § 2.4. If the hypothesis and the conclusion of a theorem have more than one part, we may interchange part of the hypothesis and part of the conclusion. Since we also call the resulting statement a converse of the original theorem, it is possible for a theorem to have more than one converse.

Both axioms and definitions also have converse statements. The converse of the postulate that all straight angles are equal is the incorrect statement that all equal angles are straight angles. A child might define a horse by the statement "A horse is an animal." In this case the converse statement that an animal is a horse is incorrect. In general, it is desirable to define mathematical terms so that the converse statement is also part of the definition. For example, a good definition of an equilateral triangle is "A triangle is *equilateral* if and only if its three sides are equal."

EXERCISES

1. Give an example of a theorem having a false converse.

2. The proof of Theorem 1 of this section is given in elementary texts without using the concept of similar triangles. Why are similar triangles not used?

3. If $\dfrac{a}{b} = \dfrac{c}{d}$, show that: $\dfrac{b}{a} = \dfrac{d}{c}, \dfrac{a}{c} = \dfrac{b}{d}, \dfrac{a}{b} = \dfrac{a+c}{b+d}$, and $\dfrac{a}{b} = \dfrac{a-c}{b-d}$.

4. If a right triangle is also isosceles, must it contain an angle of 45 degrees? If an isosceles triangle contains an angle of 45 degrees, must it be a right triangle?

1.8 EXERCISES

Most *exercises* in geometry require applications of known theorems to prove related theorems, to find numerical results, or to solve construction problems. The word **problem** usually designates an exercise involving a geometric construction. Construction problems will be introduced in § 1.9 and considered in detail in Chapter 3. Example 1, below, contains a numerical application, while Example 2 illustrates the development of material related to a known theorem.

Example 1. *In Figure 6, the perpendicular chords AB and CD intersect at P. If $AP = 3''$, $PB = 4''$, and $CP = 2''$, find the radius of circle O.*

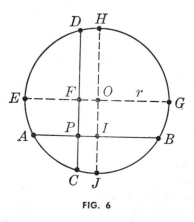

FIG. 6

Solution: By a direct application of Theorem 3 of § 1.7, it follows that the length of PD is $6''$. From O, the center of the circle through points $A,B,C,$ and D, let lines perpendicular to chords AB and CD determine points E, F, G, H, I, and J as shown. Since a radius perpendicular to a chord bisects the chord, $AI = IB = 3\frac{1}{2}$, and $CF = FD = 4$. In the rectangle $PIOF$, $PI = FO = \frac{1}{2}$, and $FP = OI = 2$. Substitution in the equality $EF \cdot FG = DF \cdot FC$ gives $(r - \frac{1}{2})(r + \frac{1}{2}) = 4 \times 4 = 16$ so that $r^2 - \frac{1}{4} = 16$ and $r = \sqrt{16.25}$.

The numerical answer can be checked by substitution in the equality $HI \cdot IJ = AI \cdot IB$ to obtain

$$HI \cdot IJ = (\sqrt{16.25} + 2)(\sqrt{16.25} - 2) = 16.25 - 4 = 12.25$$

and $$AI \cdot IB = 3\frac{1}{2} \times 3\frac{1}{2} = 12.25.$$

In the above example, $\sqrt{16.25}$ is the only possible *exact* answer. If the given conditions are only approximately satisfied, or if only an approximate answer is desired, this radical may be approximated by a suitable decimal fraction. Unless otherwise specified, exact answers are expected for numerical exercises. If only a rough approximation is needed, Example 1 can be solved by measuring a line segment in a scale drawing.

Example 2. *Show that the midpoints of consecutive sides of a quadrilateral are vertices of a parallelogram.*

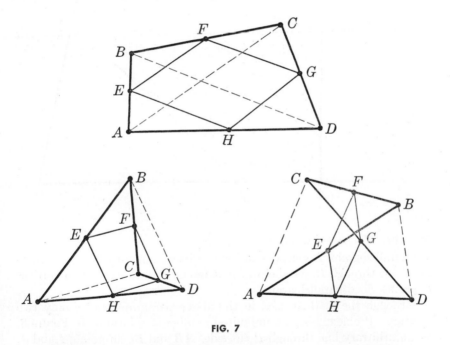

FIG. 7

The theorem is true for concave, re-entrant, and convex quadrilaterals. In each of the three diagrams shown in Figure 7, both EF and GH are parallel to AC and both FG and HE are parallel to BD, by applications of Theorem 2 of § 1.7. From the elementary theorem that two lines parallel to the same line are parallel to each other, it follows that EF and GH are parallel and also that FG and HE are parallel. The quadrilateral $EFGH$, therefore, satisfies the definition of a parallelogram.

It is possible to inscribe a parallelogram in a given quadrilateral without the vertices of the parallelogram being midpoints of the sides of the quadrilateral.

Problem 1. *Given a point P inside a quadrilateral, inscribe in the quadrilateral a parallelogram having P on one side.*

Solution: In Figure 8, $ABCD$ is the given quadrilateral. Construct a line through P, parallel to AC, to determine vertices E and F. Then construct lines through E and F, parallel to line BD, to locate vertices

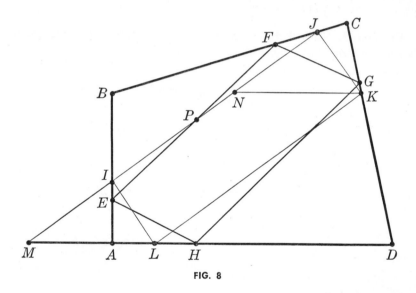

FIG. 8

H and G. Theorems 1 and 2 of § 1.7 may be used to prove that $EFGH$ is a parallelogram. A second solution can be obtained by first constructing a line through P, parallel to the diagonal BD, to locate two vertices of an inscribed parallelogram.

Although the method used in the above paragraph yields only two solutions, Problem 1 has an unlimited number of solutions. In Figure 8, let an arbitrary line through P cut sides AB and BC in points I and J, respectively. Let IJ cut line AD at M. On IJ locate point N so that $MN = IJ$. Through N construct a line parallel to AD cutting CD at K.

Through K construct a line parallel to IJ, cutting AD at L. Then $MNKL$ is a parallelogram and it follows that line segments IJ and LK are equal segments on parallel lines. This is sufficient to insure that $IJKL$ is a parallelogram.

Let the four points A, B, C, and D be given, Figure 9. These points determine six line segments AB, BC, CD, DA, AC, and BD having the respective midpoints E, F, G, H, I, and J. If these six midpoints are joined in pairs, fifteen line segments are determined; these segments form an interesting configuration.

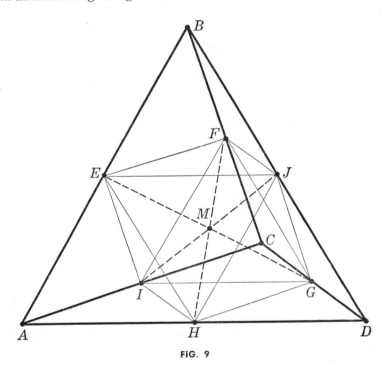

FIG. 9

Each of $EFGH$, $EJGI$, and $FJHI$ is a parallelogram; this follows from Example 2, with the proper choice of four lines to form the original quadrilateral. The three remaining line segments EG, FH, and IJ are concurrent. To prove this, let EG and FH intersect at point M. Since the diagonals of parallelogram $EFGH$ bisect each other, $EM = MG$. Since the diagonals of $EJGI$ also bisect each other, the line IJ must pass through point M.

A student with some knowledge of elementary solid geometry can extend the discussion of the above two paragraphs to cover the case in which the points A, B, C, and D (Figure 9) are not coplanar, and hence are vertices of a tetrahedron. In this case, for example, both EF and HG are parallel to AC, and half the length of AC, so that $EFGH$ is a parallelogram. It can easily be shown that the three segments joining midpoints of non-adjacent edges of a tetrahedron are concurrent at a point which bisects each segment.

EXERCISES

1. In Figure 8, let $AE = 2$, $AB = 3$, and $CG = 3$, then find GD, if $EFGH$ is a parallelogram with sides parallel to the diagonals of $ABCD$.

2. A circle has a radius of 4 inches. How long is a chord whose distance from the center is 3 inches?

3. In Figure 7, how is the perimeter of parallelogram $EFGH$ related to the length of the diagonals AC and BD?

4. Explain a method for striking a billiard ball so that, after hitting all four cushions, it will pass over the spot from which it started.

5. If, in Figure 7, $ABCD$ is a parallelogram (or a rectangle, or a square) what can be said about $EFGH$?

6. In Figure 3, let $\angle APD = 80°$, $\angle PDB = 35°$, and $\overset{\frown}{AC} = 90°$. Find the magnitude of $\overset{\frown}{DB}$.

7. If the base of a triangle is 8.6 inches and the altitude is 3.2 inches, find the area of the triangle. If the given dimensions are known to be correct to the nearest tenth of an inch only, what is the largest possible area?

1.9 ELEMENTARY CONSTRUCTIONS

The use of an unmarked straightedge and a compass in making geometric constructions has occupied a prominent place in geometry for more than two thousand years. Although there may be reasons for introducing other drawing instruments in some applications of geometry, the designing of a ruler and compass construction remains an intellectual challenge.

A *straightedge* is used to construct a line through two points. A *compass* is used to construct a circle having a given point as center and with a radius equal to the length of a given line segment. It is assumed that points of intersection of two lines, or of two circles, or of one line and one circle can be found. The solution of a construction problem requires a set of directions for combining these operations in a suitable manner; it also requires a proof that constructed elements do satisfy the required conditions.

Problem 1. *Bisect a given line segment.*

In Figure 10, AB is a given line segment and the midpoint, M, of this segment is to be found.

Construction: With A and B as centers and with a convenient radius, say r, draw arcs of circles intersecting at points C and D. Draw line CD which intersects AB at M, the required midpoint.

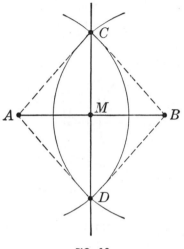

FIG. 10

Proof: Draw line segments AC, BC, AD, and BD, each of which has length r. Triangles ACD and BCD are congruent (since three sides of one are equal to three sides of the other) and the corresponding angles ACM and BCM are equal. Triangles ACM and BCM are also congruent (having two sides and the included angle equal) and it follows that AM and MB are equal.

Problem 2. *Construct a triangle, given two sides and the included angle.*

The construction is left as an exercise for the student.

Problem 3. *Construct a line through a given point parallel to a given line.*

The construction is left as an exercise for the student.

Problem 4. *From an external point, construct a line tangent to a circle.*

In Figure 11, it is required to construct a line through point P tangent to the circle with center at point O. (The circle with center at O will sometimes be called circle O.)

Construction: Bisect segment OP (Problem 1) to obtain point M. With M as center and MP as radius, construct the circle which intersects circle O in points A and B. Construct lines AP and PB; both of these lines are tangent to the given circle.

Proof: By construction $\angle OAP$ and $\angle OBP$ are both inscribed in semicircles. By Theorem 3 of § 1.5, these angles are right angles. Each of the lines PA and PB, therefore, satisfies the definition of a line tangent to circle O.

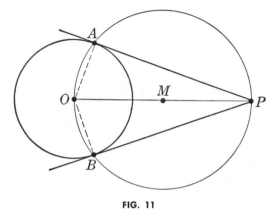

FIG. 11

It is often possible to solve a construction problem by finding a line segment whose length is related, in some specified way, to the lengths of given segments. Problem 1 was solved by finding a segment, AM, so that $AM = \frac{1}{2}AB$. Problem 4 may be solved by finding the length of a segment, PA, so that $PA = \sqrt{(OP)^2 - (OA)^2}$. For a systematic approach to this construction method, it is useful to know methods for adding, subtracting, multiplying, and dividing lengths of two given segments, and for finding a segment whose length is the square root of the length of a given segment. Since a compass can be used to transfer the length of a given line segment, finding the sum or the difference of two segments is an elementary operation. Applications of Problems 5 and 6, below, provide methods for multiplication, division, and extraction of square roots.

Problem 5. *Construct the fourth proportional to three given line segments.*

Analysis: If line segments of lengths a, b, and c are given, a segment of length x is to be constructed so that $a/b = c/x$. This can be done by applying Theorem 1 of § 1.7.

Construction: Draw two lines intersecting at point P, Figure 12. On one line mark off segments $PA = a$ and $AB = b$. On the second line mark off segment $PC = c$. Draw AC and through B construct a line parallel to AC (Problem 3) cutting PC at D. The segment CD has the desired length x.

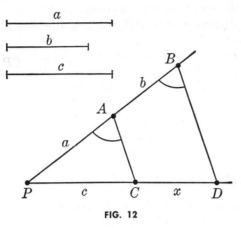

FIG. 12

This construction may be used to find either the product or the quotient of the lengths of two given line segments. Since, in Figure 12, $x = \dfrac{cb}{a}$, the product of two segments of lengths m and n can be constructed by letting $PA = 1$, $AB = m$, and $PC = n$. Likewise, the quotient of segments of lengths r and s can be constructed by choosing $PA = s$, $AB = 1$, and $PC = r$.

Problem 6. *Construct the mean proportional between two given line segments.*

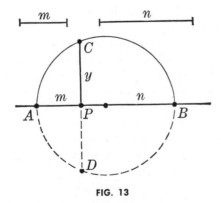

FIG. 13

Analysis: Given line segments of lengths m and n, Figure 13, it is required to construct a segment of length y so that $y = \sqrt{mn}$. Apply Theorem 3 of § 1.7, letting AB be the diameter of a circle and letting chord CD be perpendicular to AB. Then $AP \cdot PB = CP \cdot PD = (CP)^2$, or $CP = \sqrt{AP \cdot PB}$.

Construction: On a convenient line, mark off the adjacent segments $AP = m$ and $PB = n$. Construct a semicircle having AB as diameter. At P erect a perpendicular to AB, meeting the semicircle at point C. Then $CP = \sqrt{mn}$.

Proof: Complete the circle having AB as diameter, and let CP again meet this circle at D. Since CD is a chord perpendicular to the diameter AB, $CP = PD$. By Theorem 3 of § 1.7, $AP \cdot PB = CP \cdot PD$. Hence, $mn = (CP)^2$ or $CP = \sqrt{mn}$.

If a given segment has length of s, a segment with length $\sqrt{s}$ may be constructed by letting $AP = 1$ and $PB = s$ in the above construction.

EXERCISES

1. Given segments of lengths a, b, and 1, construct segments of lengths: $a + b$, $a - b$, ab, a/b, a^2, and $\sqrt{a}$. If b is greater than a, can $a - b$ be constructed?

2. Let a and b be given line segments without any indication as to the length of one unit. Line segments c, d, and e are to be constructed so that: $c = ab$, $d = a/b$, and $e = \sqrt{ab}$. Which, if any, of these line segments are independent of the choice of a unit segment?

3. Solve each of these construction problems.
    a. Bisect a given angle.
    b. From a given point, drop a perpendicular to a given line.
    c. Divide a line segment into a given number of equal parts.
    d. Inscribe a circle in a given triangle.
    e. Construct a circle passing through three given points.
    f. Trisect a right angle.
    g. Construct a regular polygon having twelve sides.

4. Given two line segments and an angle less than a straight angle, construct a triangle having the two segments as sides and the given angle as an angle. Discuss the number of possible solutions.

5. Given line segments of lengths a, b, and c, can a segment of length x be constructed so that the numerical equality $ax + b = c$ is satisfied? Does the length of x depend upon the choice of a unit segment? Can the equation $ax^2 + bx + c = 0$, where a, b, and c are given line segments, be solved by ruler and compass?

1.10 ELEMENTARY THEOREMS

This chapter is not intended as a substitute for a first geometry course; a student may, if he wishes, refer to a high school text. The elementary theorems listed below may be used for review purposes, but they were selected so that they may be used, without proof, in later portions of this book.

1. Two triangles are congruent if two sides and the included angle of one are equal respectively to two sides and the included angle of the other.
2. Two triangles are congruent if two angles and the included side of one are equal respectively to two angles and the included side of the other.
3. Two triangles are congruent if three sides of one are equal respectively to three sides of the other.
4. Two triangles are similar if two sides of one are proportional to two sides of the other and if the included angles are equal.
5. The areas of two similar polygons have the same ratio as the squares of any two corresponding sides.
6. The areas of two triangles, with equal bases, have the same ratio as their altitudes.
7. The bisector of an interior angle of a triangle divides the opposite side, internally, in the ratio of the adjacent sides.
8. The bisector of an exterior angle of a triangle divides the opposite side, externally, in the ratio of the adjacent sides.
9. Two lines parallel to the same line are parallel to each other.
10. Two lines perpendicular to the same line are parallel.
11. If three or more parallel lines intercept equal segments on one transversal, they intercept equal segments on any transversal.
12. When a transversal cuts two parallel lines the corresponding angles are equal; the alternate interior angles are equal; and the alternate exterior angles are equal.
13. Parallel lines intercept equal arcs on a circle.
14. If the sides of one angle are parallel to (perpendicular to) the sides of another angle, the angles are either equal or supplementary.
15. The diagonals of a parallelogram bisect each other.
16. The sum of the interior angles of a triangle is a straight angle.
17. The sum of the interior angles of a convex polygon with n sides is $(n - 2)$ straight angles.
18. An angle inscribed in a semicircle is a right angle.
19. The angle between two secants of a circle is measured by one-half the difference of the intercepted arcs.
20. If two secants are drawn from the same point outside a circle, the product of one secant and its external segment is equal to the product of the second secant and its external segment.
21. In the same circle, or in equal circles, chords equidistant from the center are equal.
22. A diameter which is perpendicular to a chord of the circle bisects the chord.

23. If two angles of a triangle are equal, the sides opposite these angles are equal.

24. The sum of any two sides of a triangle exceeds the third side; the difference between any two sides is less than the third side.

25. In a right triangle the sum of the squares of the two legs is equal to the square of the hypotenuse.

26. The medians of a triangle are concurrent.

27. The bisectors of the interior angles of a triangle are concurrent.

28. The bisectors of two exterior angles of a triangle and the bisector of the opposite interior angle are concurrent.

29. The altitudes of a triangle are concurrent.

30. The perpendicular bisectors of the sides of a triangle are concurrent.

31. If P is a point inside a circle, the locus of the midpoints of all chords through P is a circle.

32. The locus of points at a given distance from a given line consists of two lines parallel to the given line.

33. The locus of points equidistant from two given points is the perpendicular bisector of the segment joining the points.

34. The locus of points equidistant from two intersecting lines consists of the two lines which bisect the angles between the intersecting lines.

35. The locus of points from which equal tangents can be drawn to a circle is a circle concentric with the given one.

EXERCISES

1. Prove Theorem 3 of this section.

2. Prove Theorem 11 of this section.

3. Find, in this section, a theorem with a false converse and prove that the converse is false.

4. In Theorem 31 of this section, where is the center and what is the radius of the circular locus?

5. Sketch and label figures, then state what is given and what is to be proved in each of Theorems 8, 12, 19, 24, and 28 of this section.

6. In triangle ABC, $AB = 6$, $BC = 5$, and $CA = 4$. If the bisector of angle ACB cuts AB at D, find the length of segment DB.

7. Construct a line parallel to a given line and tangent to a given circle.

REVIEW EXERCISES

A set of review exercises is given at the end of each of the first nine chapters of this book. Some of the exercises are marked by stars to indicate that solutions may require information not given in this text.

1. Prove that tangents drawn to a circle from an external point are equal.

2. Given a circular arc, construct the entire circle.

3. Prove Theorem 19, § 1.10.

4. Prove that the area of a rhombus is equal to one-half the product of its diagonals.

5. A quadrilateral is inscribed in a circle. What is known about its opposite angles?

6. A triangle has sides of 4, 5, and 3 inches. A second triangle, which is similar to the first one, has a perimeter of 20 inches. Is this enough information to determine the area of the second triangle?

7. Consider the three hypotheses:

   H1. To get a good grade, a person must study.

   H2. A and B are good grades.

   H3. Jane received a grade of B in geometry.

   Is the following conclusion valid?

   C. Jane studied.

8. Construct a parallelogram, given the two diagonals and one side.

9. State necessary and sufficient conditions for: (a) a quadrilateral to be a parallelogram; (b) two triangles to be congruent; (c) two triangles to be similar; (d) three points to lie on a circle.

10. If the hypothesis or the conclusion of a theorem has more than one condition, a converse may be obtained by interchanging one condition of the conclusion with one condition of the hypothesis. State two possible converses for the theorem "A line joining midpoints of two sides of a triangle is parallel to and equal to one-half of the third side." Does this theorem have any true converse?

★11. Use mathematical induction to prove Theorem 17, § 1.10.

★12. How is the Theorem of Pythagoras, Theorem 25 of § 1.10, a special case of the Law of Cosines?

★13. For two similar polyhedrons make the statements concerning the ratio of volumes that are space generalizations of Theorems 5 and 6 of § 1.10.

★14. For Theorems 31, 32, 33, 34, and 35 of § 1.10, suggest corresponding space loci.

★15. What is the locus, in a plane, of points equidistant from a given point and from a given line?

2

Directed Elements

2.1 DIRECTED LINE SEGMENTS

In Chapter 1 numerical quantities were restricted to positive values only. Since college students have used directed lines and angles in trigonometry and analytic geometry, it seems reasonable to extend the definitions of measurements of geometric quantities to include negative numbers. In the following definitions the word *distance* is used when a direction is involved while the word *length* refers to an undirected segment.

Definition 1. *On any line, one direction may be chosen as positive; the opposite direction is negative.*

On a horizontal line, the direction from left to right will be positive unless otherwise specified. In general, the same positive direction will be assigned to two parallel lines.

Definition 2. *The symbol AB denotes the directed distance from point A to point B. If the direction from A to B coincides with the positive direction along the line through A and B, AB is a positive number equal to the length of the line segment AB expressed in the chosen unit of measure; in the opposite case AB is a negative number. If A and B are coincident points, AB is zero, and conversely.*

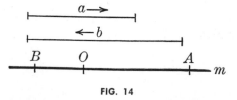

FIG. 14

If AB is a directed segment, it follows that $AB = -BA$. In Figure 14, distances BO, OA, and BA are positive while distances OB, AO, and AB

28

are negative. The following definition will be used when adding two directed segments which lie on the same or on parallel lines.

Definition 3. *If two directed segments, AB and BC, are placed on the same line so that the initial end of the second coincides with the terminal end of the first, the sum, AC, of the segments is the distance from the initial end of the first segment to the terminal end of the second: $AB + BC = AC$.*

In Figure 14, the addition of two line segments is illustrated. The segments a and b lie on parallel lines with arrows indicating that a is positive and b is negative. By construction, on line m, $OA = a$ and $AB = b$. Then $a + b = OB$, where the sum is negative.

Since two distinct points determine a line, three given points usually determine three lines. It is, therefore, of interest to find conditions which require three or more points to lie on the same line. For example, in analytic geometry, the equation of a line through two fixed points may be found by setting up conditions which guarantee that an arbitrary point be on the line determined by the two given points. In a similar way it is possible to motivate the consideration of other theorems giving relationships such as those which show when three lines are concurrent or when four points are on the same circle.

Theorem 1. *If three points A, B, and C are collinear then, using directed segments, $AB + BC = AC$.*

Although the truth of Theorem 1 is a consequence of Definition 3, the theorem is explicitly stated both for future reference and to suggest a discussion of its converse. Let A, B, and C be three given points; on each line determined by these points assign a direction so that AB, BC, and AC are directed distances. Since the sum $AB + BC$ has been defined only if the segments AB and BC are on the same line, the converse of Theorem 1 cannot be used to show that the given points are collinear. Let the positive lengths of segments AB, BC, and AC be c, a, and b, respectively. Then the points A, B, and C are collinear if $a + b = c$, or if $a - b = c$, or if $b - a = c$. The student should be able to verify this using the elementary theorem that in a triangle the length of one side must be greater than the difference between the other sides and less than the sum of the other sides.

Definition 4. *If P is any point on the line through the points A and B, P is said to divide the segment AB in the ratio AP/PB.*

If P is between A and B, the ratio AP/BP is positive, since AP and PD must have the same sign. If P divides the segment AB externally, the ratio AP/PB is negative.

Problem 1. *Divide a line segment in the ratio of two given segments.*

Analysis: Given the segment AB, Figure 15, and directed segments m and n, a point P can be constructed on AB so that $AP/PB = m/n$ by an application of Theorem 1, § 1.7.

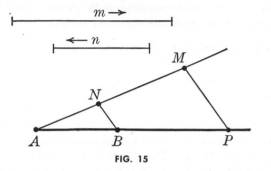

FIG. 15

Construction: Draw any convenient line through A and on this line lay off $AM = m$ and $MN = n$, where AM and MN have like directions if m and n have like signs and opposite directions if m and n have unlike signs. Draw line NB and through M construct a line, parallel to NB, cutting AB at point P which divides AB in the desired ratio.

The proof is left as an exercise for the student who should show that the given construction is valid for all possible directed segments m and n, except for $m = -n$.

EXERCISES

1. Solve Problem 1 by first laying off directed segments m and n on a line parallel to the given segment AB.

2. Solve Problem 1 by drawing parallel lines through A and B and marking off segment m on one line and segment n on the other.

3. Why is the construction, given for Problem 1, not valid when the ratio of the given segments is -1? Are the solutions suggested in Exercises 1 and 2, above, valid for this special case?

4. If A, B, C, and D are collinear, does it necessarily follow that $AB + BC + CD + DA = 0$?

5. Prove that the interior and exterior bisectors of an angle of a triangle divide the third side internally and externally in the same ratio.

2.2   IDEAL ELEMENTS

In Definition 4 of § 2.1, the ratio in which P divides the segment AB is not properly defined when P and B coincide, since the denominator of AP/PB is then zero. The construction of a point dividing a line segment in a given ratio, Problem 1 of § 2.1, is impossible when the ratio is -1, since no finite point P exists on line AB so that the directed distances AP and BP are equal. However, as P recedes farther and farther along the line AB, the ratio between the lengths of AP and BP becomes more nearly equal to one; in the notation of elementary calculus $\lim_{AP \to \infty} \dfrac{AP}{PB} = -1$. These considerations lead to the following definitions and postulate.

Definition 1. *On each line there is one and only one point called an* **ideal point;** *the ideal point is assumed to be at an infinite distance from each other point of the line.*

Definition 2. *If A and B are fixed points, $AP/PB = -1$ if and only if P is the ideal point on line AB.*

The definition of ideal points places one additional point on each of the lines previously considered in Euclidean geometry and makes possible a useful modification of Postulate l, § 1.4.

Postulate 1. *Two distinct lines, in the same plane, intersect in one and only one point; the point is an ideal point if and only if the lines are parallel.*

The introduction of ideal points does not require a change in the postulate that two points determine one line. Since, however, two ideal points determine a special line, the following definition is introduced.

Definition 3. *In a plane there is one and only one line called the* **ideal line** *which is the locus of all ideal points in the plane.*

Theorem 1. *For any real constant r and any line segment AB, there exists one and only one point P on AB so that $AP/PB = r$.*

Proof: If $r = -1$, P is the ideal point on AB. For any other value of r the construction given in Problem 1, § 2.1, locates one point P so that $AP/PB = r$. To show that there is only one point satisfying the conditions, assume that P and Q are two points on the segment AB for which $AP/PB = AQ/QB$. Use of Theorem 1, § 2.1, gives

$$\frac{AP}{PB} = \frac{AQ + QP}{PQ + QB} = \frac{AQ}{QB}.$$

Ordinary operations of algebra, combined with properties of directed segments give

$$AQ \cdot QB + QP \cdot QB = AQ \cdot PQ + AQ \cdot QB,$$

$$QP \cdot QB = -QP \cdot AQ,$$

$$QP(AQ + QB) = 0,$$

and $$QP(AB) = 0.$$

Since $AB \neq 0$ it follows that $QP = 0$ so that P and Q coincide.

Directed line segments may be used to combine several theorems of elementary geometry into one more general result. The following example contains Theorem 3, § 1.7, and Theorem 20, § 1.10, as special cases.

Theorem 2. *If one line through a point P cuts a circle at points A and B and if a second line through P cuts the circle at C and D, then*

$$PA \cdot PB = PC \cdot PD.$$

Proof: Case 1. If P is inside the circle this is Theorem 3, § 1.7, where both of the products $PA \cdot PB$ and $PC \cdot PD$ are negative.

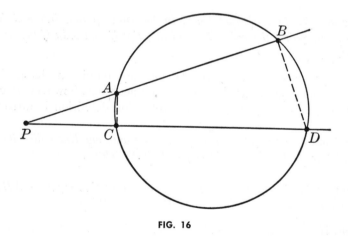

FIG. 16

Case 2. If P is outside the circle, Figure 16, both products will be positive and it is sufficient to show that $PA/PC = PD/PB$ for un-directed segments. These ratios will be equal if triangles PAC and PDB are directly similar. Since the angle at P is common, the triangles are similar if $\angle PAC = \angle PDB$. By Theorem 3, § 1.5, $\angle PDB$ is measured by one-half of arc CAB. By a limiting case of Theorem 4, § 1.5, $\angle PAC$ is also measured by one-half of arc CAB.

EXERCISES

1. Is your solution for Exercise 2, of § 2.1, valid when $m/n = -1$?

2. The symbol A_∞ is sometimes used to designate an ideal point. If A_∞ is a point on a horizontal line through the point B, does A_∞ lie to the right or to the left of B?

3. A specific ideal point may be designated by showing a line segment on which the ideal point lies. Construct a line through a given ideal point and tangent to a given circle.

4. On a line segment AB construct points P so that $AP/PB = r$ for $r = 3$, $r = -3$, $r = \frac{1}{3}$, and $r = -\frac{1}{3}$.

5. Let P be a point on a horizontal line segment AB with B to the right of A. If $AP/PB = r$, describe the variation in r as P moves along the entire line through A and B.

6. If a quadrilateral is inscribed in a circle, prove that opposite angles are supplementary.

7. Prove that the tangents to a circle from an external point are equal.

8. If ideal elements were to be defined in three-dimensional space, suggest a definition for the ideal plane.

9. If a tangent and a secant are drawn from one point, prove that the tangent is the mean proportional between the secant and its external segment. How can this theorem be used to construct a line through a point tangent to a circle?

2.3   DIRECTED ANGLES

In plane geometry, angles are not ordinarily assigned directions and that convention will be followed in this book unless it is clearly stated that directed angles are being considered. One objection to general use of directed angles is that this requires modifications in the statements of numerous familiar theorems. For example, the statement that an exterior angle of a triangle is equal to the sum of the two opposite interior angles must be re-examined if the angles may be either positive or negative. A general definition of a directed angle is given below; for a specific application a different definition might be desirable.

Definition 1. *A **directed angle**, $\angle ABC$, is generated by the rotation of a line about the vertex B from the position of the initial side BA to that of the terminal side BC; if $\theta = \angle ABC$ is the measure of this rotation, in degrees, θ is **positive** if the rotation is counterclockwise and **negative** if the rotation is clockwise.*

If A, B, and C are any three points, and if $\theta = \angle ABC$, the **principal value** of θ is taken greater than -180 degrees and less than or equal to $+180$ degrees. The general value of θ is its principal value plus $360n$ where n is an arbitrary integer.

Several elementary theorems relating the magnitude of an angle to the arcs intercepted on a circle may be combined into a single statement if directed arcs are defined in a manner consistent with the definition of directed angles.

Definition 2. *Circular arcs are* **positive** *if traced counterclockwise and* **negative** *if traced clockwise.*

In Figure 17, $\angle BOD$ is negative. As line AB rotates about O, until it coincides with line CD, it sweeps out negative arc BD and positive

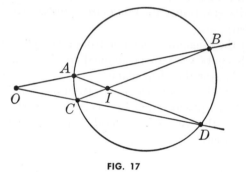

FIG. 17

arc AC. The positive angle BIA intercepts arcs BA and CD, each of which is positive. With this interpretation, earlier theorems are combined in the following statement, given without proof.

Theorem 1. *The directed angle between two lines is measured by one-half the sum of the directed arcs intercepted by the lines on any circle.*

Additional definitions are necessary to specify the directed angle between two directed lines, or the angle of intersection of a directed line and a circle. For example, the angle between two directed lines may be defined by calling their point of intersection B, placing point A on the first line and C on the second, so that both of the segments AB and BC are positive, then assigning to the angle between the lines the value of $\angle ABC$ given in Definition 1. Changing the direction of one line increases or decreases this angle by 180 degrees. If each side of a triangle is assigned a positive direction, the sum of the directed angles in the triangle RST may be interpreted as the sum of the three angles between the pairs of lines RS and ST, ST and TR, TR and RS. This sum may be either $+180°$ or $-180°$.

EXERCISES

1. In Figure 17, $\widehat{BD} = 2\widehat{CA}$ and $\angle AIB = -100°$. How large is $\angle COA$?

2. Give a definition of the directed angle of intersection of two circles. Does the definition give equal angles at both intersections?

3. Without using directed angles, state special cases of Theorem 1 in which the two lines intersect: outside the circle, on the circle, inside the circle, and at the center of the circle. Also mention possible cases in which one or both lines are tangent to the circle.

4. Some definition is necessary to associate the measure of angles with the measure of circular arcs. Could Theorem 1 be stated as such a definition (and thus require no proof)?

5. If points A, B, and C lie on a straight line, with B between A and C, show that $\angle ABC \neq - \angle CBA$ if principal values are used.

6. If A, B, C, and D are arbitrary points, show that $\angle ABC + \angle CBD$ is not necessarily equal to $\angle ABD$ when principal values are used.

2.4 CYCLIC QUADRILATERALS

Definition 1. *Four or more points which lie on the same circle are* **concyclic.**

Definition 2. *A* **cyclic quadrilateral** *is a quadrilateral which can be inscribed in a circle.*

Numerous necessary and sufficient conditions for a quadrilateral to be cyclic are known. The three theorems which follow contain conditions related to previous work.

Theorem 1. *A convex quadrilateral is cyclic if and only if two opposite angles are supplementary.*

Proof: For the first part of the proof let $ABCD$, Figure 18, be inscribed in a circle. From Theorem 3, § 1.5, it follows that $\angle A + \angle C = 180°$ and also that $\angle B + \angle D = 180°$.

For the second part of the proof, assume that in quadrilateral $ABCD$, Figure 18, $\angle B + \angle D = 180°$. Construct the circle through points A, B, and C. The vertex D must be inside this circle, or outside this circle, or on this circle. If D is inside the circle, use of Theorem 4, § 1.5, produces the contradictory result $\angle B + \angle D > 180°$. Likewise, if D is outside the circle, Theorem 19 of § 1.10 shows that $\angle B + \angle D < 180°$. Hence D must lie on the circle through A, B, and C.

Theorem 2. *A convex quadrilateral is cyclic if and only if one side subtends the same angle at the two opposite vertices.*

The proof of Theorem 2 is left as an exercise for the student, who must show that $ABCD$, Figure 18, is cyclic if $\angle ADB = \angle ACB$ and conversely.

Theorem 3. *Let any opposite sides, say AB and CD, of a quadrilateral intersect at a point S. The quadrilateral $ABCD$ is cyclic if and only if $SA \cdot SB = SC \cdot SD$.*

Proof: If the quadrilateral $ABCD$, Figure 18, is cyclic, Theorem 2 of § 2.2 states that $SA \cdot SB = SC \cdot SD$ where the segments involved are directed and S may be either inside or outside the circle (the quadrilateral $ABCD$ may be re-entrant).

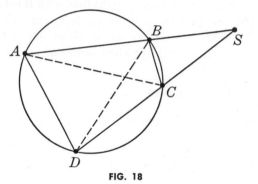

FIG. 18

If points A, B, C, and D are given points with S on both AB and CD and if $SA \cdot SB = SC \cdot SD$, construct the circle through points A, B, and C. Let SC cut this circle at X. From the first part of this proof it follows that $SA \cdot SB = SC \cdot SX$. From these equalities it may be shown that $SD = SX$, and since these equal directed segments have the same initial point the terminal points D and X must coincide. Hence A, B, C, and D are on the same circle.

The work presented heretofore has consisted of review topics or simple extensions of elementary material. In the remainder of this chapter several theorems of a more advanced nature are considered. The discovery of Theorem 4 is sometimes attributed to a Scottish mathematician, Robert Simson (1687 − 1768).

Theorem 4. *From any point on the circumcircle of a triangle the three perpendiculars to the sides of the triangle meet the sides in collinear points.*

Given: In Figure 19, P is on the circle through A, B, and C. Angles PLB, PMC, and PNA are right angles.

To prove: The points L, M, and N lie on the same line.

Analysis: Use properties of cyclic quadrilaterals to show that angles *PNM* and *PNL* are equal.

Proof: The proof will be completed when it is demonstrated that $\angle PNM = \angle PNL$. Construct lines *PA*, *PB*, and *PC*. Since quadrilateral *PNBL* is cyclic, $\angle PNL = \angle PBL$, by Theorem 2. It is given

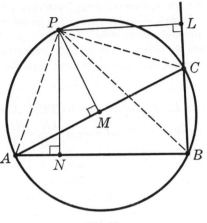

FIG. 19

that the quadrilateral *ABCP* is cyclic so that $\angle PBL = \angle PAC$. In right triangle *PAM*, angles *PAC* and *MPA* are complementary. In cyclic quadrilateral *ANMP*,

$$\angle ANM = 90° + \angle PNM = 180° - \angle MPA$$

$$\angle PNM = 90° - \angle MPA = \angle PAC$$

Thus $\angle PNM = \angle PNL$ since each is equal to $\angle PBL$.

EXERCISES

1. State necessary and sufficient conditions for five (or more) points to be concyclic.

2. Which theorems of this section were proved using an indirect method?

3. Prove this converse of Theorem 4. If *L*, *M*, and *N* are collinear points on the sides of triangle *ABC* and if the three perpendiculars to the sides at these points are concurrent at a point *P*, then *P* lies on the circumcircle of triangle *ABC*.

4. If the conditions of Exercise 3 are met, line *LMN* is called the Simson line of point *P*. Let *L* be any point on side *BC* of triangle *ABC*. Construct all possible Simson lines which pass through *L*.

5. If P, Figure 19, coincides with vertex B, where is the corresponding Simson line?

2.5 THEOREM OF MENELAUS

Theorem 4, § 2.4, contains one set of conditions for which three points located on the sides of a triangle are collinear. Necessary and sufficient conditions for three points, one on each side of a triangle, to be collinear can be expressed in terms of the six directed segments in which these points divide the sides of the triangle. Theorem 1, below, is named for **Menelaus** of Alexandria, an astronomer and mathematician, who is credited with discovering the theorem about 100 A.D.

Theorem 1. *Points L, M, and N on sides BC, CA, and AB respectively of triangle ABC are collinear if and only if $\dfrac{AN}{NB} \cdot \dfrac{BL}{LC} \cdot \dfrac{CM}{MA} = -1$.*

Proof: A line not through a vertex, must divide two sides internally and one side externally or else it must divide all three sides externally. In either case, the product in the theorem must be negative since an odd

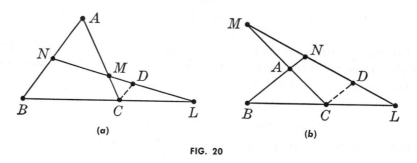

FIG. 20

number of the factors are negative. In Figure 20 let LMN be a straight line and construct a line through C, parallel to AB, cutting LM at D. From similar triangles LCD and LBN, neglecting directions, it follows that

$$\frac{LC}{BL} = \frac{DC}{NB} \quad \text{or} \quad DC = \frac{LC \cdot NB}{BL}.$$

From similar triangles DCM and NAM it follows that

$$\frac{DC}{AN} = \frac{CM}{MA} \quad \text{or} \quad DC = \frac{CM \cdot AN}{MA}.$$

Equating the two expressions for DC, and taking directions into account, gives the desired result

$$\frac{AN}{NB} \cdot \frac{BL}{LC} \cdot \frac{CM}{MA} = -1.$$

Conversely, if

$$\frac{AN}{NB} \cdot \frac{BL}{LC} \cdot \frac{CM}{MA} = -1$$

let the line through points L and N cut CA at M'. Then since

$$\frac{AN}{NB} \cdot \frac{BL}{LC} \cdot \frac{CM'}{M'A} = -1$$

it follows that

$$\frac{CM}{MA} = \frac{CM'}{M'A}$$

and by Theorem 1, § 2.2, points M and M' must coincide.

The Theorem of Menelaus may be used, as in Theorem 2 below, to show that three special points on the sides of a triangle are collinear; it also has other applications some of which will be considered later.

Theorem 2. *The interior bisectors of two angles of a triangle and the exterior bisector of the third angle meet the opposite sides in three collinear points.*

Proof: In Figure 21, let AL and CN be bisectors of the interior angles at A and C and let BM be the bisector of the exterior angle at B. Let

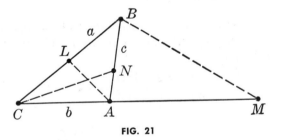

FIG. 21

a, b, and c be the lengths of sides BC, CA, and AB respectively. Use of Theorems 7 and 8, § 1.10, gives

$$\frac{AN}{NB} = +\frac{b}{a}, \quad \frac{BL}{LC} = +\frac{c}{b}, \quad \text{and} \quad \frac{CM}{MA} = -\frac{a}{c}.$$

Hence

$$\frac{AN}{NB} \cdot \frac{BL}{LC} \cdot \frac{CM}{MA} = -\frac{b \cdot c \cdot a}{a \cdot b \cdot c} = -1$$

so that, by Theorem 1, L, M, and N are collinear.

EXERCISES

1. Is the Theorem of Menelaus true if transversal MN is parallel to side BC?

2. Prove that the exterior bisectors of the angles of a triangle meet the opposite sides in three collinear points.

3. The six bisectors of the angles of a triangle meet the opposite sides in six points. How many straight lines pass through at least three of those points?

4. In Figure 20, let N be the midpoint of AB and let C be the midpoint of BL. If AC is 14 inches, find the length of MC.

5. Let L, M, and N be three collinear points on the sides BC, CA, and AB of triangle ABC. Let A', B', and C' be the midpoints of sides BC, CA, and AB. Let L', M', and N' be points on BC, CA, and AB so that $LA' = A'L'$, $MB' = B'M'$, and $NC' = C'N'$. Prove that $L'M'N'$ is a straight line.

2.6 THEOREM OF CEVA

The Theorem of **Ceva** is a generalization of several elementary theorems concerning concurrent lines associated with a triangle. It is credited to the Italian mathematician Giovanni Ceva who, in 1678, published a book containing both Theorem 1, below, and the Theorem of Menelaus, § 2.5, which seems to have been forgotten and then rediscovered by Ceva. The proof below shows that these two theorems are related.

Theorem 1. *Three lines drawn from vertices A, B, and C of triangle ABC and meeting the opposite sides in points L, M, and N respectively are concurrent if, and only if,*

$$\frac{AN}{NB} \cdot \frac{BL}{LC} \cdot \frac{CM}{MA} = +1.$$

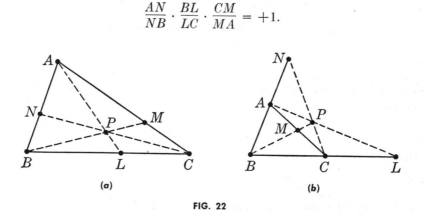

(a)   (b)

FIG. 22

Proof: In Figure 22, let AL, BM, and CN be concurrent at point P. Let BPM be a transversal of triangle ALC and apply the Theorem of Menelaus, Theorem 1 of § 2.5. Then

$$\frac{AP}{PL} \cdot \frac{LB}{BC} \cdot \frac{CM}{MA} = -1.$$

Likewise, consider CPN as a transversal of triangle ABL to obtain

$$\frac{AN}{NB} \cdot \frac{BC}{CL} \cdot \frac{LP}{PA} = -1.$$

Multiplication of the members of the above equalities, with rearrangement and regard for directed segments, gives the desired result

$$\frac{AN}{NB} \cdot \frac{BL}{LC} \cdot \frac{CM}{MA} = +1.$$

The converse may be proved by the indirect method used in the proof of the Theorem of Menelaus.

The Theorem of Ceva may be used to prove that the medians, or the altitudes, or the bisectors of the interior angles of a triangle are concurrent. For example, if L, M, and N are midpoints of the sides, each of the three ratios in Ceva's Theorem has the value 1 so that the product of the ratios is also 1.

The three bisectors of the interior angles of a triangle meet in a point called the **incenter** of the triangle (Exercise 1, page 42). The bisector of two exterior angles and the bisector of the third interior angle meet in a point called an **excenter** of the triangle (Exercise 3, page 42). There are exactly four distinct circles tangent to all three sides of a given triangle; the circle having the incenter for its center is called the **inscribed circle** (or **incircle**); the three circles with centers at excenters are called **excircles.**

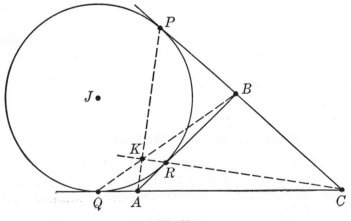

FIG. 23

The center, J, of the excircle shown in Figure 23, is the intersection of the bisectors of the exterior angles A and B of triangle ABC, and the bisector of the interior angle at C. If this circle is tangent to the sides of the triangle at points P, Q, and R as shown, the lines AP, BQ, and CR are concurrent. To prove this assertion it is sufficient to show that

$$\frac{AQ}{QC} \cdot \frac{CP}{PB} \cdot \frac{BR}{RA} = +1.$$

Since two tangents to a circle from the same point have equal lengths, it follows that $AQ = RA$, $QC = CP$, and $PB = BR$. Substitution, with proper regard for the sign, shows that the product under consideration must have the value $+1$. This result is stated below as Theorem 2.

Theorem 2. *Lines joining the vertices of a triangle to the points of contact of an excircle are concurrent.*

EXERCISES

1. Prove that the bisectors of the interior angles of a triangle are concurrent.

2. Prove that the altitudes of a triangle are concurrent.

3. Prove that the bisectors of two exterior angles of a triangle and the bisector of the third interior angle are concurrent.

4. In triangle ABC, N is the midpoint of AB and C is the midpoint of BL. If M is a point on CA so that the lines AL, CN, and BM are concurrent at P, describe the location of the points M and P.

5. Prove that the lines joining the points of contact of the inscribed circle to the opposite vertices of the triangle are concurrent.

6. Show that the medians of a triangle intersect in a point two-thirds of the distance from one vertex to the midpoint of the opposite side.

7. Let $ABCP$ be a parallelogram. Apply Ceva's Theorem, combined with properties of ideal points, to show that the diagonals of a parallelogram bisect each other.

8. Is Theorem 2 likely to be found in a secondary school geometry text? Why?

2.7 APPLICATIONS OF THE THEOREMS OF CEVA AND MENELAUS

Let L, M, and N, on sides BC, CA, and AB respectively of triangle ABC, satisfy Ceva's Theorem, § 2.6. Let X be a point on side AB so that points L, M, and X satisfy the Theorem of Menelaus, § 2.5. By Theorem 1, § 2.6,

$$\frac{AN}{NB} \cdot \frac{BL}{LC} \cdot \frac{CM}{MA} = +1$$

and by Theorem 1, § 2.5

$$\frac{AX}{XB} \cdot \frac{BL}{LC} \cdot \frac{CM}{MA} = -1$$

These two relations yield the equality

$$\frac{AN}{NB} = -\frac{AX}{XB}$$

which shows that points N and X divide the segment AB internally and externally in the same ratio. The Theorems of Ceva and Menelaus may, therefore, be used to solve the following construction problem, using a straightedge only.

Problem 1. *Given the collinear points A, B, and C, find a fourth point D so that points B and D divide the segment AC internally and externally in the same ratio.*

Construction: In Figure 24, draw convenient lines through A and C intersecting at E. Draw a line through B intersecting CE at L and AE

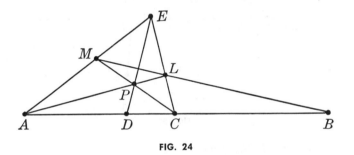

FIG. 24

at M. Draw lines AL and CM intersecting at P. Draw EP intersecting AC at D. Applying the Theorems of Ceva and Menelaus to triangle ACE shows that $AB/BC = -AD/DC$.

It is possible to start with three points, on the sides of a triangle, which satisfy the Theorem of Ceva (or of Menelaus) and by a simple transformation of some or all of the points produce a new set of points satisfying the theorem.

Notation: A special notation, used in the remainder of this section, is illustrated in Figure 25. The notation (L,M,N) means that L, M, and N are fixed points on the sides BC, CA, and AB, respectively, of triangle ABC. The points (A',B',C') are midpoints of sides BC, CA, and AB. The circle through L, M, and N again cuts the sides of the triangle in points (L'',M'',N''). The points L, M, and N are reflected about the midpoints of the respective sides to obtain the points (L',M',N'). That is,

$$LA' = A'L', \quad MB' = B'M', \quad \text{and} \quad NC' = C'N'.$$

Let points L and X divide BC internally and externally in the same ratio. Obtain Y and Z from M and N in a corresponding manner so that points (X,Y,Z) satisfy the relations

$$\frac{BL}{LC} = -\frac{BX}{XC}, \quad \frac{CM}{MA} = -\frac{CY}{YA}, \quad \text{and} \quad \frac{AN}{NB} = -\frac{AZ}{ZB}.$$

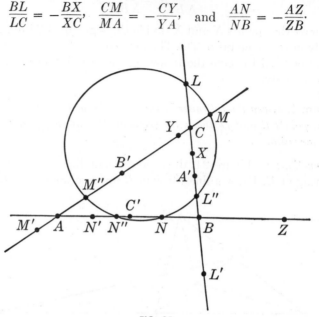

FIG. 25

For fixed points (L,M,N) let

$$k = \frac{AN}{NB} \cdot \frac{BL}{LC} \cdot \frac{CM}{MA}.$$

From the definition of (L',M',N') it follows that $AN = N'B$, $NB = AN'$, $BL = L'C$, $LC = BL'$, $CM = M'A$, and $MA = CM'$. Hence

$$\frac{AN'}{N'B} \cdot \frac{BL'}{L'C} \cdot \frac{CM'}{M'A} = \frac{NB}{AN} \cdot \frac{LC}{BL} \cdot \frac{MA}{CM} = \frac{1}{k}.$$

Likewise, from properties of (X,Y,Z), it follows that

$$\frac{AN}{NB} \cdot \frac{BX}{XC} \cdot \frac{CY}{YA} = \frac{AZ}{ZB} \cdot \frac{BL}{LC} \cdot \frac{CY}{YA} = \frac{AZ}{ZB} \cdot \frac{BX}{XC} \cdot \frac{CM}{MA} = k.$$

If $k = 1$, these results show that each of the sets of points (L,M,N), (L',M',N), (X,Y,N), (L,Y,Z), and (X,M,Z) satisfies the Theorem of Ceva. Likewise, if $k = -1$, each of these sets satisfies the Theorem of Menelaus.

In Figure 25, let

$$\frac{AN}{NB} \cdot \frac{BL}{LC} \cdot \frac{CM}{MA} = 1.$$

By use of Theorem 3, § 2.4, and the above-mentioned properties of points (L'', M'', N''), it can be shown that

$$AN \cdot AN'' = MA \cdot M''A, \quad BL \cdot BL'' = NB \cdot N''B,$$

and $$CM \cdot CM'' = LC \cdot L''C.$$

These relations are equivalent to

$$\frac{AN}{MA} = \frac{M''A}{AN''}, \quad \frac{BL}{NB} = \frac{N''B}{BL''}, \quad \text{and} \quad \frac{CM}{LC} = \frac{L''C}{CM''}.$$

A rearranged product of the members of the last three equalities gives

$$\frac{AN}{NB} \cdot \frac{BL}{LC} \cdot \frac{CM}{MA} = \frac{N''B}{AN''} \cdot \frac{L''C}{BL''} \cdot \frac{M''A}{CM''} = 1$$

or $$\frac{AN''}{N''B} \cdot \frac{BL''}{L''C} \cdot \frac{CM''}{M''A} = 1$$

so that points (L'', M'', N'') satisfy Ceva's Theorem. These results are now collected in Theorems 1 and 2.

Theorem 1. *If points* (L, M, N) *satisfy the Theorem of Menelaus, so do points* (L, Y, Z), (X, M, Z), (X, Y, N), *and* (L', M', N').

Theorem 2. *If points* (L, M, N) *satisfy Ceva's Theorem, so do points* (L, Y, Z), (X, M, Z), (X, Y, N), (L', M', N'), *and* (L'', M'', N'').

EXERCISES

1. Use straightedge and compass to solve Problem 1, without reference to theorems of Ceva or Menelaus.

2. Solve Problem 1 for the case in which B divides AC internally. Check the accuracy of the construction by using two different triangles for ACE, Figure 24.

3. Draw a triangle and locate points (L, M, N) as the points where bisectors of the interior angles of the triangle cut the opposite sides. Find points X, Y, Z, L', M', N', L'', M'', and N'' and the points of intersection of five sets of three concurrent lines as an illustration for Theorem 2.

4. In Theorem 2, let (L, M, N) be midpoints of the sides. Describe the location of points X, Y, Z, L', M', and N'. Construct points (L'', M'', N'') and see if they seem to coincide with the feet of the altitudes.

REVIEW EXERCISES

1. Points P and Q divide a segment AB internally and externally in the same ratio. If $AB = +6$ and $QA = +5$, find the directed length of segment BP.

2. Through a point P, outside a circle, construct a line cutting the circle at points A and B so that $PA = AB$.

3. The shortest distance from a point P, outside a certain circle, to the circumference of the circle is 3. A line through P cuts the circle in points X and Y. If $PX = 4$ and $XY = 2$, find the radius of the circle.

4. In the triangle ABC, $AB = 7$, $BC = 8$, and $CA = 10$. The bisector of the exterior angle at A cuts BC at P. Find the length of the segment BP.

5. The points A, B, C, and D are concyclic. If $AB = 6$, $AC = 5$, $CB = 4$, and if CD bisects angle ACB, find the length of CD.

6. Why is it not possible to use Ceva's Theorem in proving that the perpendicular bisectors of the sides of a triangle are concurrent?

7. The angle between two intersecting lines, tangent to a certain circle, is 120°. Find the magnitude of the minor arc intercepted on the circle.

8. In triangle ABC let m_a be the median from A, let t_b be the bisector of angle B, etc. Let m_a and t_b intersect at X and let CX cut AB at L. Let m_b and t_c intersect at Y and let AY cut BC at M. Let m_c and t_a intersect at Z and let BZ cut CA at N. Are the lines CL, AM, and BN concurrent?

★9. Let A have co-ordinates $(0,0)$, let B have co-ordinates $(b,0)$, and let P have co-ordinates $(x,0)$. If k is the ratio AP/PB, solve for k in terms of b and x. Solve this relation for x in terms of b and k.

★10. Solve exercise 9 if k is the ratio AP/AB.

★11. Given the circle $(x - 2)^2 + y^2 = 1$ and the point $P(0,0)$, show that if any line through P cuts the circle at A and B, then $PA \cdot PB = 3$. Illustrate this by finding the co-ordinates of A and B when $y = x/4$. Might the property $PA \cdot PB = 3$ also hold for imaginary points of intersection? For the line $y = x$, find the co-ordinates of A and B, and attempt to evaluate the product $PA \cdot PB$.

★12. Line segments having lengths and directions specified are called vectors and have important applications in representing forces. Give a definition for the sum of two coplanar vectors and find the vector sum of two vectors, with different directions, by straightedge and compass.

3

Ruler and Compass Constructions

~~~~~~

3.1 SOLUTION OF CONSTRUCTION PROBLEMS

Solving a construction problem may be compared to the playing of a game in which certain equipment is employed and uniform rules are enforced; some students prefer the analogy to a battle in which modern weapons are outlawed. Traditionally, the equipment used in geometric constructions is restricted to the unmarked straightedge (sometimes called a ruler) and the compass.

Logically there would be no objection to employing additional instruments in making geometric constructions if proper "rules" were given for the use of such devices. The use of construction equipment may, if desired, be limited to something even more restricted than a ruler and compass. The study of constructions using the compass only (or using the straightedge only) has been highly developed and isolated examples of such constructions will be inserted throughout this book.

An acceptable solution of a construction problem contains:

1. Directions for making the construction using ruler and compass;
2. Proof the construction is correct;
3. Discussion of special cases and the number of solutions.

The solution may also include one or more alternate construction methods and a discussion of a more general problem or of a related problem. These steps say nothing about the actual drawing of a geometric configuration, although in practice the directions in the solution are usually followed to produce a corresponding figure. It is to be remembered that the solution of a construction is an exact logical process in which, for example, lines have no thickness, so that any drawing can only be an approximation to a solution.

Many students seem to think that almost every mathematical problem has one and only one solution. A proposed construction problem may have no solution, a finite number of solutions, or an unlimited number of solutions. In applications persons often ask a mathematician to solve problems which, in contrast to most textbook problems, are poorly stated and lack essential information. Other problems may contain unnecessary or even contradictory data.

It is wise to consider whether or not a problem has more than one solution at the beginning of an attempt to find a solution; the number of solutions can, in many cases, be determined without knowing how to find any solution. If only one solution exists, a solution found by any method will completely solve the problem. If more than one solution exists, it may be that only a specified one of these solutions is desired, so that a method for finding this particular solution should be sought.

A few college students still spend time trying to find a ruler and compass method for trisecting any given angle, although they have been told that a solution for this problem has been proved impossible. Correct methods for trisecting a general angle require special instruments not allowed in the usual geometry course. In most incorrect solutions, a student mistakes an approximate solution for an exact one, or else he invents some new "rules." The trisection problem is discussed in § 12.3.

Solutions of construction problems are not always easy. It may be difficult to decide how to start an analysis which will lead to a solution. This, however, presents a challenge which can make the solution of a construction problem one of the most interesting features of geometry. The present chapter does not present a general method for attacking every problem, but it does contain methods that have wide applications.

EXERCISES

1. Comment on the statement that geometry consists of correct reasoning about incorrect figures.

2. Illustrate the fact that the number of solutions to a construction problem depends on special cases by sketching two circles so that the number of common tangents is exactly: (a) none, (b) one, (c) two, (d) three, and (e) four.

3. At one end-point of a given line segment construct a perpendicular, without extending the given segment.

4. Let a compass be adjusted to draw a circle with a fixed radius and then make no additional adjustments. Using this "rusty" compass and a straightedge tell how to: (a) bisect a line segment; (b) bisect an angle; (c) drop a perpendicular from a given point to a given line.

5. Let A be a point on the circumference of a circle with center O. Construct, using a compass only, a point B so that AB is a diameter of the given circle.

3.2 PRODUCT OF CHORDS

It has been noted earlier that constructions will be used to motivate the introduction of related material. In most texts, constructions are used primarily to illustrate applications of theorems; and it is, indeed, appropriate to ask if a theorem has applications, direct or indirect, to construction problems, new or old. As an illustration, consider Theorem 2 of § 2.2; a special case of this theorem shows that in Figure 26 where

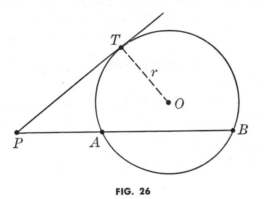

FIG. 26

PT is tangent to circle O, $(PT)^2 = PA \cdot PB$. This relation may be used to provide solutions for several construction problems considered earlier. The solution of Problem 4, § 1.9, contains two methods for constructing a tangent to a circle from an external point. For a third method, draw a line through the given point P, Figure 26, cutting the circle in points A and B. Then construct PT, the mean proportional between PA and PB, as in Problem 6, § 1.9. With P as center and PT as radius, swing an arc cutting the circle in the two points of contact of the tangents through P.

The mean proportional between two line segments, Problem 6, § 1.9, can also be found by use of Theorem 2, § 2.2. Given two segments of lengths m and n, with $n > m$, choose any convenient circle and mark off a chord AB of length m. Extend AB and locate P on this line, with A between P and B, so that $PB = n$. Through P construct a line tangent to the circle at point T. Then PT is the mean proportional between m and n.

Since the two construction problems mentioned above have been solved previously by elementary methods, someone may ask why these constructions were discussed again. It is unlikely, but not impossible, that a beginning student will discover unknown theorems or constructions in plane geometry. He may, however, enjoy some of the satisfaction of creative thinking by finding proofs and constructions that are new to him.

Theorem 2, § 2.2, can also be used to solve construction problems which have not been mentioned previously in this book. Suppose, for example, that in Figure 26, the circle and its center are erased but that three of the four points P, A, B, and T are left. Can the circle O be reconstructed? The points A, B, and T immediately determine circle O. If points P, T, and A (or P, T, and B) are given, the point B (or A) can be found by use of Theorem 2, § 2.2. The points P, A, and B do not determine T uniquely, but T can be found if the direction of the line PT is known. This suggests the following related problem and its solution.

Problem 1. *Construct a circle passing through two given points and tangent to a given line.*

Construction: Let line t (Figure 27) be a given line and let A and B be given points on the same side of line t with line AB cutting t in the ordinary point P. Use Problem 6, § 1.9, to construct a line segment of length $x = \sqrt{PA \cdot PB}$. With P as center and x as radius, describe an arc cutting t at points T and T'. The circle O through A, B, and T

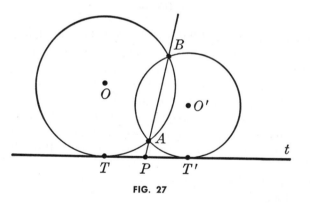

FIG. 27

is one solution and points A, B, and T' determine the second circle O'.

Proof: To show that circle O is a solution, it is sufficient to show that circle O is tangent to line t at point T. This follows from the construction by use of Theorem 2, § 2.2.

Number of solutions: For A and B on the same side of t, and for AB not parallel to t, two solutions have been constructed. No other solution exists, since if any circle through points A and B is tangent to line t at a point R, it follows that $PA \cdot PB = (PR)^2$ and that R must coincide with T or with T'.

Special cases: If AB is parallel to t, the given construction is not valid, since P is then an ideal point. In this case, let the perpendicular bisector of the segment AB cut t at S. The circle through A, B, and S is the only solution with a finite radius, although the line AB may be considered as a solution tangent to t at the ideal point on t. If points A and B are on opposite sides of the line t, there is no solution, since any circle through A and B must necessarily cut line t. (Do you suppose it would be possible to define an "imaginary" circle which would be a solution in this case?)

Ordinarily, even in discussing special cases, given elements will be taken as distinct. The student may, however, verify that when points A and B coincide an unlimited number of solutions are possible. If one point is on t, only one solution exists; this is a limiting case in which the two solutions have become the same circle. If both A and B are on t, there is no solution unless the line t is considered as the limiting position for the two possible solutions.

Related problems: In Problem 1, replace the given points by circles to obtain this generalization: "Construct a circle tangent to two given circles and also tangent to a given line." A solution for this new problem would give a solution to Problem 1 for the limiting case in which the radius of each given circle was zero. A problem similar to Problem 1, but neither a generalization nor a special case, is "Construct a circle through a given point tangent to two given lines." These and similar problems will be discussed later.

EXERCISES

1. How many circles exist tangent to three given lines? Discuss all special cases.

2. Give two or more methods for constructing a line through a given point parallel to a given line.

3. Construct a circle with a given radius passing through a given point and tangent to a given line.

4. Two angles and one side of a triangle are given. What is the greatest possible number of triangles, having these component parts, if no two solutions are congruent?

5. In Figure 26, show that $r = \sqrt{(OP)^2 - PA \cdot PB}$.

3.3 CONSTRUCTION OF REGULAR POLYGONS

The preceding section suggests that one powerful method for solving construction problems is to anticipate the problem before someone asks for a solution. This method of "planning for the future" obviously has applications in fields other than mathematics. When confronted by a specific problem, with which he is not familiar, a student must resort to other methods. Although it is impossible to give precise rules for the solution of every problem, some suggestions may be helpful. Certainly one must understand exactly what is given and what is to be constructed. It may be helpful to sketch an approximate figure showing the desired configuration and from this attempt to find useful relationships connecting the given data and the desired result.

As mentioned in § 1.9, some problems can be solved by finding an expression for the length of a desired line segment in terms of lengths of known segments. The solution of the following problem is an additional example showing the usefulness of this method.

Problem 1. *Inscribe a regular decagon in a given circle.*

Analysis: Let the given circle, Figure 28, have center O and radius r. Assume that chord AX is one side of the required polygon of ten sides. Then angle $AOX = 36°$ and the problem can be solved either by constructing an angle of $36°$ or by constructing a segment of length AX.

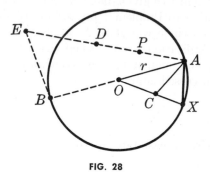

FIG. 28

With A as center and AX as radius, swing an arc cutting OX at C. Since $\angle ACX = \angle AXC = 72°$, it follows that $\angle OAC = 36° = \angle AOC$. Since triangle OAC is isoceles, $OC = AC$. From corresponding sides of similar triangles we find that $OX/AX = AC/CX$. Replacing CX by $r - OC$, and using $AX = AC = OC$, this becomes

$$\frac{r}{AX} = \frac{AX}{r - AX}$$

which is equivalent to $(AX)^2 + r(AX) - r^2 = 0$. This equation has the positive solution

$$AX = \frac{r(\sqrt{5} - 1)}{2}.$$

When r is given, the segment AX may be constructed by the methods of § 1.9.

Construction: Draw a diameter AB of the given circle. At B erect a line perpendicular to AB and locate E on this line so that $BE = r$, where r is the radius of the given circle. With E as center and r as radius, swing an arc cutting EA at D. Bisect DA to locate point P. The segment AP is the length of one side of the desired decagon.

Proof: By construction, $AB = 2r$ and $EB = r$. By the Theorem of Pythagoras, Theorem 25 of § 1.10, $EA = r\sqrt{5}$. Since $ED = r$, it follows that $DA = r\sqrt{5} - r$ and $AP = \frac{1}{2}r(\sqrt{5} - 1)$. In the analysis it was shown that this is the length of one side of an inscribed decagon.

Related problems: A regular pentagon can be constructed by joining alternate vertices of a regular decagon. The vertices of a regular polygon of 20 sides can be found by bisecting the ten arcs determined by the vertices of a regular decagon. Likewise it follows that from a regular polygon of k sides, a regular polygon of $k \cdot 2^n$ sides can be constructed for any positive integer n.

In constructing a regular decagon, a central angle of 36° is obtained. By subtracting an angle of 30° (found by bisecting an angle of an equilateral triangle) an angle of 6° is obtained. Bisecting this angle gives an angle of 3°, so that a regular polygon of n sides may be constructed by ruler and compass whenever $3n$ is a factor of 360.

The above discussion, combined with well-known elementary methods, shows how to construct regular polygons of 3, 4, 5, 6, 8, 10, 12, 15, 16, 20, 24, and 30 sides. The great German mathematician, Carl Friedrich Gauss (1777–1855), when only seventeen years old, showed how to construct a regular polygon of 17 sides. He proved that if p is a prime number the five smallest values of p for which a regular polygon of p sides can be constructed are 3, 5, 17, 257, and 65537. This ended (or should have ended) a period of some 2000 years in which persons tried to construct a regular heptagon ($p = 7$) by ruler and compass. A statue of Gauss, erected in Goettingen after his death, had a seventeen-sided regular polygon for its pedestal.

EXERCISES

1. Inscribe a regular hexagon in a circle of radius r. What is the length of one side? What is the area of the hexagon?

2. Construct a line segment of length $\sqrt{5} - \sqrt{7}$ when a unit segment is given.

3. Explain a method for constructing a regular polygon of 15 sides.

4. Is the following construction of a regular pentagon (or of a five-

pointed star) exact? At O, the midpoint of diameter AB, erect a perpendicular cutting the circle at C. Bisect OB at E. With E as center and EC as radius cut AO at F. Step CF around the circle five times to obtain the desired vertices.

5. Is the following construction of a five-pointed star exact? Take five equally spaced collinear points, say A, B, C, D, and E in order. Let the line through C perpendicular to AE cut the circle with center D and radius DA at the points Q and R. Let QE and RE cut this circle at S and T. Join the points Q, R, T, A, S, and Q in order by line segments.

6. If a person in charge of a Christmas program asked you to make a pattern to be used for cutting out five-pointed stars, would you use the method of Exercise 4, the method of Exercise 5, or a different method?

3.4   OTHER CONSTRUCTION METHODS

One frequently used method for solving a mathematical problem is that of successively changing the problem to a different but equivalent form until it becomes a problem whose solution is known. This is, for example, the basic method used in solving an algebraic equation. The method can often be applied in solving construction problems. In the following problem, the construction of a line tangent to two circles is reduced to the familiar problem of constructing a tangent to a circle from an external point.

Problem 1. *Construct a common tangent to two given circles.*

Given: Let the given circles, Figure 29, have centers A, B and radii a and b respectively with $b > a$.

First analysis: Suppose that a common external tangent is to be con-

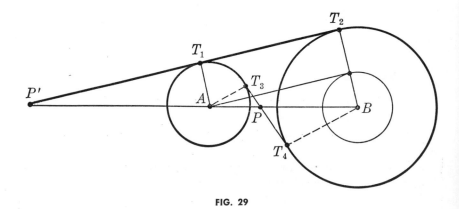

FIG. 29

structed. Assume that T_1T_2 is such a solution. A line through A parallel to T_1T_2 will be tangent to the circle with center B and radius $b - a$. Likewise a line through A, parallel to the common internal tangent T_3T_4, will be tangent to a circle with center B and radius $b + a$.

Second analysis: Suppose the desired tangent is an internal one, say T_3T_4 in Figure 29. If T_3T_4 cuts AB at P, then from similar triangles $AP/PB = a/b$, so that P divides AB internally in the ratio a/b. The point P can be located, Problem 1, § 2.1, and the line through P tangent to one circle will be tangent to the other. Likewise, the common external tangent divides the segment AB externally in the ratio a/b.

Further details of the construction and proof are omitted, since these follow directly from the analysis. The number of possible common tangents is: none, if one circle is inside the other; one, if the circles are internally tangent; two, if the circles intersect; three, if the circles are externally tangent; and four otherwise.

The solution of many construction problems depends upon the proper location of one or more points. As an elementary example, consider the problem of locating a point X so that X is at a given distance, d, from a point P and also the same distance, d, from a line l. Disregarding l, it is seen that X must lie on a circle with center P and radius r. Disregarding P, it is seen that X must be on one of the two lines parallel to l at a distance d from l. If these loci intersect, they determine the desired point X. There may be two, one, or no solutions. Because of the usefulness of locus theorems in analyzing and solving construction problems, Chapter 4 will be devoted to a study of geometric loci.

The ideas in the above paragraph may be extended somewhat to provide another powerful method for attacking a construction problem. The method involves disregarding one of the conditions which a solution must satisfy and then finding all solutions which satisfy the remaining conditions. It may then be possible to pick out one of these solutions which also satisfies the condition disregarded earlier. This process is illustrated below.

Problem 2. *Given two intersecting lines r and s and a point P, locate a point R on r and a point S on s so that P is the midpoint of the segment RS.*

Analysis: In Figure 30 disregard line s at first. Let R_1 be any point on r. Extend R_1P to S_1 so that $R_1P = PS_1$. Pick R_2 on r and double R_2P to locate S_2. Pick R_3 on r and double R_3P to locate S_3. The points S_1, S_2, and S_3 appear to lie on a straight line parallel to line r. This suggests the following construction.

Construction: Let S_1 and S_2 be constructed as in the analysis and let line S_1S_2 cut s at S. Let SP cut r at R. Then P is the midpoint of segment RS.

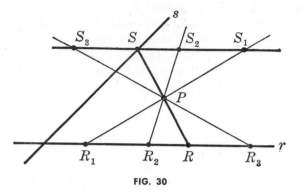

FIG. 30

Proof: The triangles R_1PR_2 and S_1PS_2 are congruent, since two sides and the included angle of one are equal to two sides and the included angle of the other. It follows that the line S_1S_2S is parallel to line r. Triangles R_1PR and S_1PS are congruent, since $\angle RR_1P = \angle SS_1P$, $\angle R_1PR = \angle S_1PS$, and $R_1P = S_1P$. Hence the corresponding sides SP and RP are equal.

EXERCISES

1. Let d be the distance between centers of two **circles** with radii r_1 and r_2. If $r_2 > r_1$, and if $r_1 + r_2 < d$, find the lengths of the common tangents to the circles.

2. Given three circles with equal radii, construct at least one circle tangent to the three given circles.

3. Through a given point, construct a line on which a given circle cuts off a chord having a given length.

4. Inscribe a square in an equilateral triangle so that one side of the square lies along one side of the triangle and the other two vertices of the square lie on the other two sides of the triangle.

5. You will recall that a *parabola* is the locus of points equidistant from a fixed point, the *focus*, and a fixed line, the *directrix*. Although it is impossible to draw a parabola with ruler and compass, show how to construct points on a parabola when the focus and directrix are given.

REVIEW EXERCISES

1. Construct a triangle, given the midpoints of its sides.

2. Construct a triangle given one angle, the opposite side, and the median from the given angle to the opposite side.

3. Construct a triangle similar to a given one and having a given perimeter.

4. In a given circle, construct a chord of given length parallel to a second given chord.

5. Given two intersecting lines r and s and a point P, locate R on r and S on s so that R is the midpoint of PS.

6. In a circle inscribe a triangle similar to a given one.

★7. If a, b, and c are given directed line segments, construct a segment x so that $ax^2 + bx + c = 0$.

★8. Can two linear equations be solved simultaneously by ruler and compass? For example, if a, b, c, d, e, and f are given segments, can segments of lengths x and y be constructed so that $ax + by = c$ and $dx + ey = f$?

★9. Find the equation of a circle tangent to the x-axis and passing through the points (0,3) and (2,1).

★10. In analyzing a construction problem it is found that the problem can be solved by finding an angle θ so that

$$\tan \theta = \frac{a - b \cos \phi}{\sin \phi}$$

where a and b are given directed segments and ϕ is a given angle. Can angle θ be constructed by ruler and compass?

4

Geometric Loci

~~~~~~

4.1 DEFINITION OF LOCUS

Finding the location of a specific point in relation to other data may be considered the fundamental operation in the solution of construction problems. Each construction is made by a succession of steps involving the drawing either of a straight line or of a circle; both of these steps depend on the proper location of points to determine the line or to fix the position of the center of the circle. The usual way to locate a point is to find the intersection of two lines, or of two circles, or of one line and one circle. For example, the center of the circle inscribed in a triangle is found by bisecting two interior angles of the triangle; the center of the circle circumscribed about the triangle is the intersection of the perpendicular bisectors of two sides. For this reason, the knowledge of theorems describing geometric loci can be very useful in the solution of construction problems.

Loci which do not consist of straight lines or circles have limited applications in geometric constructions and are usually omitted in the study of plane geometry. Perhaps one reason that analytic geometry, but not synthetic Euclidean geometry, is included in the typical college mathematics sequence is that the loci of analytic geometry are not restricted to straight lines and circles.

Definition 1. *The geometric **locus** of a point, which satisfies certain given conditions, is a figure which (a) contains all points that satisfy the given conditions, and (b) contains no other points.*

The proof that an assumed locus is correct consists of showing that both parts of Definition 1 are satisfied. Hence to prove a locus theorem it is necessary and sufficient to (a) prove that every point satisfying the given conditions lies on the locus, and (b) prove that every point on the locus satisfies the given conditions.

The theorems considered in this chapter are chosen in view of later applications to construction problems. For this reason, each proof is preceded by directions for constructing the locus with ruler and compass. The proofs show that each point on the constructed locus satisfies the given conditions and that every point satisfying the given conditions is on the constructed locus. The first theorem is suggested by Theorem 18, § 1.10.

Theorem 1. *The locus of points from which a given line segment subtends a right angle is the circle having the given segment as diameter.*

Construction: If in Figure 31, AB is the given segment, bisect AB to locate O. The desired circular locus has center O and radius OA.

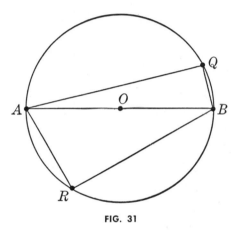

FIG. 31

Proof: Let Q be any point on the circumference of the constructed circle. By Theorem 18, § 1.10, angle AQB is a right angle. Let R be any point for which angle ARB is a right angle. Then R must be on circle O, for if R is inside the circle angle ARB is greater than a right angle by Theorem 4, § 1.5. Likewise, if R is outside the circle angle ARB is less than a right angle by Theorem 19, § 1.10.

Theorem 1 has the following generalization which is suggested by Theorem 3 of § 1.5.

Theorem 2. *The locus of points, on one side of a given line segment, from which the given segment subtends a given angle is a circular arc whose end-points are the extremities of the given segment.*

Construction: Let AB, Figure 32, be the given segment and let angle C be the given angle. The desired arc can be constructed after one point on the arc, other than A or B is determined. One way to find a suitable third point is to locate the midpoint, P, of the desired arc AB. The point P must lie on the line through A which makes an angle of $90° - C/2$ with AB; it must also lie on the perpendicular bisector of segment AB.

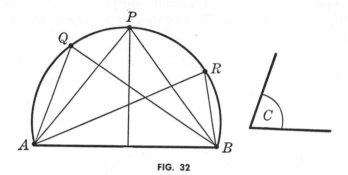

FIG. 32

Proof: Let Q be any point on the constructed arc. Then by Theorem 3, § 1.5, $\angle AQB = \angle APB = \angle C$. Next suppose that R is a point, on the proper side of AB, so that $\angle ARB = \angle C$. As in the proof of Theorem 1, if R is either inside or outside the circle constructed through points A, P, and B, angle ARB cannot equal angle C. Hence R must be on the constructed locus.

Problem 1. *Construct a triangle given one side, the angle opposite, and the ratio in which the interior bisector of the given angle cuts the given side.*

Analysis: In Figure 33, let side a and angle A be given. Let b/c be the ratio in which the bisector of angle A cuts side a. Assume that triangle ABC is the desired solution. Point D can be found by dividing

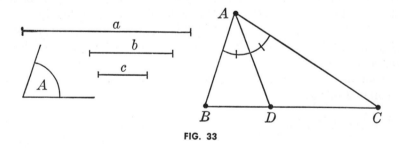

FIG. 33

BC in the ratio b/c. One locus containing vertex A is the circular arc from which BC subtends angle A, Theorem 2. A second locus containing A is the circular arc from which BD subtends one-half of angle A.

Details of the construction and proof are left as exercises.

Problem 2. *Determine a point inside a triangle from which each side of the triangle subtends an angle of 120°.*

Analysis: In Figure 34, if P is on the arc AB and $\angle APB = 120°$, then arc AB can be constructed by use of Theorem 1. In fact, arc AB contains 120° and the center, O, of this arc is outside triangle ABC with $\angle ABO = \angle BAO = 30°$. In the same manner, the desired circular arc BC can be constructed. These arcs, through the common point B, meet in a second point P, which is inside triangle ABC if and only if each

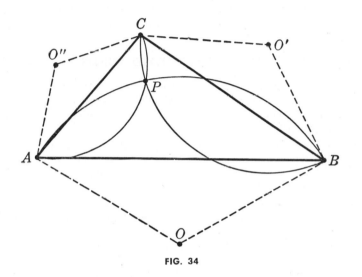

FIG. 34

interior angle of the triangle is less than 120°. If an interior angle is greater than 120°, no solution exists for Problem 2. Otherwise point P is the desired point.

Proof: By construction, $\angle APB = \angle BPC = 120°$. When P is inside the triangle, $\angle APB + \angle BPC + \angle CPA = 360°$. It follows that angle CPA contains 120° also.

EXERCISES

1. To prove a locus theorem is it necessary and sufficient to: (*a*) prove that every point on the locus satisfies the given conditions, and (*b*) prove that every point not on the locus does not satisfy these conditions?

2. Point out an error in each of the following statements. (*a*) The locus of the tip of a clock pendulum is a circle, since the tip is always a fixed distance from the pivot point of the pendulum. (*b*) The locus of points equidistant from two lines is the line which bisects the angle

between the lines, since each point on the bisector is the same distance
from the two sides of the angle.

3. Provide proofs for Theorems 32, 33, 34, and 35 of § 1.10.

4. Use Theorem 1 of the present section to prove Theorem 31 of § 1.10.

5. Make a suitable modification of Definition 1 to provide a definition
of the locus of a line. Describe the locus of a line a fixed distance from a
given point.

6. Construct a triangle given one side, the opposite angle, and a line
segment whose length is numerically equal to the area of the triangle.

7. Construct a circle, with a given radius, and tangent both to a given
line and to a given circle. Discuss the number of possible solutions.

4.2   LOCI ASSOCIATED WITH TWO FIXED POINTS

One of the most familiar of all locus theorems is the statement that the locus
of points equidistant from two fixed points is the perpendicular bisector of the
segment joining the points. There are numerous locus theorems concerning the
path of a point which moves so that its distances from two fixed points satisfy
certain conditions. Some students who recall that an *ellipse* is the locus of
points the sum of whose distances from two fixed points is a constant, and that a
hyperbola is the locus of points the difference of whose distances from two fixed
points is a constant, may be surprised to learn that certain loci, determined by
conditions which seem more complex, are circles and straight lines. The circular
locus in Theorem 1, below, is called the *circle of Apollonius,* in honor of the
last of the famous Greek geometers. Apollonius, who died about 200 B.C., is
especially noted because of his synthetic geometry treatment of conic sections.

Theorem 1. *The locus of a point the ratio of whose distances from two
fixed points is constant is a circle, called the circle of Apollonius.*

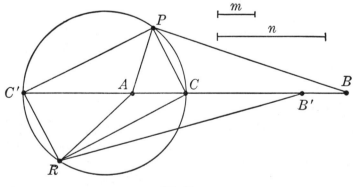

FIG. 35

Construction: Given points A and B, Figure 35, and two line segments
m and n, the locus of P is to be constructed so that $PA/PB = m/n$,

where undirected segments are used. For the special case, $m = n$, the constant ratio has the value one and the locus is the straight line which is the perpendicular bisector of segment AB. For $m \neq n$, construct points C and C' dividing AB internally and externally in the ratio m/n, Problem 1 of § 2.1. The circle with CC' as diameter is the desired locus.

Proof: Let P be any point for which $PA/PB = m/n$. Since $AC/CB = m/n$, the point C divides side AB of triangle ABP internally in the ratio of the adjacent sides and it follows that PC bisects angle APB, Theorem 7 of § 1.10. Likewise, using Theorem 8 of § 1.10, PC' is the exterior bisector of angle APB. Since the interior and exterior bisectors of an angle are perpendicular, Theorem 1 of § 4.1 shows that P must lie on the constructed locus.

Conversely, if R is any point on the circle with CC' as diameter, angle CRC' is a right angle. To complete the proof it is sufficient to show that $AR/RB = AC/CB$, which must be true if RC bisects angle ARB. That RC does bisect angle ARB can be demonstrated by constructing a line through R, cutting AB at B', so that $\angle ARC = \angle CRB'$ and then showing that B and B' coincide. Since CR and $C'R$ are perpendicular, $C'R$ is the exterior bisector of angle ARB', so that $AC/CB' = AC'/C'B'$. Since, by construction, $AC/CB = AC'/C'B$ it follows that, for undirected segments, $\dfrac{CA}{AC'} = \dfrac{CB}{BC'} = \dfrac{CB'}{B'C'}$. This means that B and B' divide the segment CC' in the same numerical ratio. Since B and B' both divide CC' externally, Theorem 1 of § 2.2 shows that B and B' coincide.

Theorem 2. *The locus of points, the difference of the squares of whose distances from two given points is constant, is a straight line perpendicular to the given segment.*

Analysis: If points A and B, Figure 36, and a real number k are given, the desired locus will contain each point for which, in terms of the chosen unit of length, $(AP)^2 - (BP)^2 = k$. To find the points in which the locus cuts line AB, let C be any point on AB for which $(AC)^2 - (CB)^2 = k$. By Theorem 1 of § 2.1, $CB = AB - AC$, so that

$$(AC)^2 - (CB)^2 = (AC)^2 - (AB - AC)^2 = -(AB)^2 + 2(AB)(AC) = k.$$

Hence

$$AC = \frac{k + (AB)^2}{2(AB)}$$

and the real number AC uniquely determines the directed segment AC.

Construction: The segment of length AC may be constructed from the given data and point C, on AB, is uniquely determined. At C erect a line CX perpendicular to AB to obtain the desired locus.

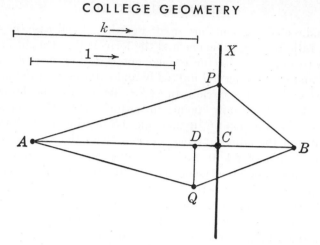

FIG. 36

Proof: Let P be any point on CX. Using the theorem of Pythagoras, and the fact that P is on the constructed locus, one finds

$$(AP)^2 - (PB)^2 = (AC)^2 + (CP)^2 - (CP)^2 - (CB)^2$$
$$= (AC)^2 - (CB)^2 = k.$$

Hence any point on CX satisfies the given conditions.

Conversely, let Q be any point for which $(AQ)^2 - (QB)^2 = k$ and let the perpendicular from Q cut AB at D. Then

$$(AQ)^2 - (QB)^2 = (AD)^2 + (DQ)^2 - (DQ)^2 - (DB)^2$$
$$= (AD)^2 - (DB)^2 = k.$$

This shows that D is on the desired locus. In the analysis it was shown that C is the only point on AB satisfying the given conditions and so C and D coincide. It follows that Q lies on CX.

Theorem 3. *The locus of points, the sum of the squares of whose distances from two given points is equal to a given constant, is a circle having for its center the midpoint of the given segment.*

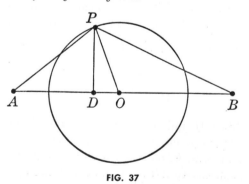

FIG. 37

Analysis: Let k be a given positive constant. In Figure 37, let O be the midpoint of the given segment AB. Let P be any point for which $(AP)^2 + (PB)^2 = k$. Let the perpendicular from P cut AB at D. Two applications of the theorem of Pythagoras give

$$(PD)^2 = (AP)^2 - (AD)^2 = (OP)^2 - (DO)^2$$

so that

$$(AP)^2 = (OP)^2 + (AD)^2 - (DO)^2 = (OP)^2 + (AD + DO)(AD - DO).$$

Replacing $AD + DO$ by AO, and AD by $AO - DO$, leads to

$$(AP)^2 = (OP)^2 + (AO)(AO - 2DO) = (OP)^2 + (AO)^2 - 2(AO)(DO).$$

In the same manner it follows that

$$(BP)^2 = (OP)^2 + (BO)^2 - 2(BO)(DO).$$

Now add the members of the last two equalities, and replace BO by $-AO$, to obtain

$$(AP)^2 + (BP)^2 = 2(OP)^2 + 2(AO)^2.$$

Hence

$$(OP)^2 = \frac{(AP)^2 + (BP)^2}{2} - (AO)^2$$

so that

$$(OP)^2 = \frac{k}{2} - \frac{(AB)^2}{4} \quad \text{or} \quad OP = \tfrac{1}{2}\sqrt{2k - (AB)^2}.$$

Since O is a fixed point and $OP = \tfrac{1}{2}\sqrt{2k - (AB)^2} = r$ is a constant, it follows that the locus for P is the circle with center O and with radius r.

Construction: If $k < \tfrac{1}{2}(AB)^2$, there is no real locus. If $k > \tfrac{1}{2}(AB)^2$, the radius $r = \tfrac{1}{2}\sqrt{2k - (AB)^2}$ can be constructed from the given data. The desired locus is the circle with center at the midpoint of segment AB and with radius r.

EXERCISES

1. In Theorem 2, describe the location of C on AB, for $k = 0$, for $k = (AB)^2$, and for $k = -2(AB)^2$.

2. In Figure 37, let the length of AB be one unit, and let $(AP)^2 + (PB)^2 = 4$. Construct the locus of point P.

3. Given three collinear points A, B, and C, in order, construct the locus of a point P so that $\angle ABP = \angle BPC$.

4. Given four collinear points, A, B, C, and D, in order, find a point P so that $\angle APB = \angle BPC = \angle CPD$.

5. Construct triangle ABC given side a, the altitude from vertex A, and the ratio b/c.

4.3 CONCURRENT PERPENDICULARS

The Theorem of Ceva, § 2.6, has been used both to simplify proofs of several well-known elementary theorems and also to provide additional theorems related to concurrent lines passing through the three vertices of a triangle. This section contains an analogy in which the three concurrent lines do not pass through vertices but are perpendicular to the sides of the triangle. The desired theorem will be developed by drawing perpendiculars, from a fixed point, to divide each side of the triangle into two segments. A relation connecting these six segments will be obtained and then, conversely, it will be shown that if points divide three sides of a triangle in this special manner the perpendiculars to the sides at these points must be concurrent.

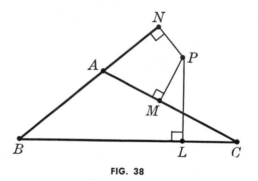

FIG. 38

In Figure 38, ABC is a given triangle and P is an arbitrary fixed point. The perpendiculars from P to sides BC, CA, and AB of triangle ABC meet these sides in points L, M, and N respectively. From Theorem 2, § 4.2, it follows that

$$(PC)^2 - (PB)^2 = (LC)^2 - (BL)^2,$$
$$(PA)^2 - (PC)^2 = (MA)^2 - (CM)^2,$$

and
$$(PB)^2 - (PA)^2 = (NB)^2 - (AN)^2.$$

By adding the members of these equalities, we obtain

$$(BL)^2 + (CM)^2 + (AN)^2 = (LC)^2 + (MA)^2 + (NB)^2$$

as a necessary condition for L, M, and N to be feet of perpendiculars from the same point.

The converse may be proved by the usual indirect method of letting perpendiculars at L and M intersect at P, letting the perpendicular from P cut AB at N' and then showing that N and N' coincide.

The results of the previous analysis are contained in Theorem 1.

Theorem 1. *Let L, M, and N be points on sides BC, CA, and AB, respectively, of triangle ABC. The three lines perpendicular to BC, CA, and AB at points L, M, and N are concurrent if and only if,*

$$(BL)^2 + (CM)^2 + (AN)^2 = (LC)^2 + (MA)^2 + (NB)^2.$$

EXERCISES

1. Use Theorem 33, § 1.10, to prove that the perpendicular bisectors of the sides of a triangle are concurrent.

2. Supply details of the proof that the equality of Theorem 1 is sufficient to insure that the corresponding perpendiculars are concurrent.

3. Use Theorem 1 to verify the following statements.

   a. The perpendicular bisectors of the sides of a triangle are concurrent.

   b. The altitudes of a triangle are concurrent.

   c. Perpendiculars erected to the sides of a triangle at the points of contact of an excircle are concurrent.

4. Let points L, M, and N satisfy Theorem 1. Let L', M', and N' be reflections of L, M, and N about the midpoints of the sides on which they are located, as in § 2.7. Do the points L', M', and N' also satisfy the conditions of Theorem 1?

5. Let the circle through points L, M, and N again intersect sides BC, CA, and AB in points L'', M'', and N''. If L, M, and N satisfy Theorem 1, must L'', M'', and N'' also satisfy this theorem?

REVIEW EXERCISES

1. Construct a circle with a given radius, with its center on a given line, and tangent to a given circle.

2. Construct a circle with a fixed radius, tangent to two given circles. Make a sketch indicating that eight solutions may exist if the given circles intersect. Show that under special conditions an unlimited number of solutions may exist.

3. Construct triangle ABC given side AB, the altitude from B to AC, and angle C.

4. Given two concentric circles and an angle, construct the locus of points from which lines tangent to the two circles intersect in the given angle.

5. Let perpendiculars to the sides BC, CA, and AB, of triangle

ABC, at points L, M, and N respectively, be concurrent. Are the lines LA, MB, and NB also concurrent? Show that the answer is "yes" if L, M, and N are: midpoints of the sides, feet of the altitudes, points of contact of the incircle, or points of contact of an excircle.

★6. Use analytic geometry to find the equation of the locus of points equidistant from a given point and from a given line.

★7. Let A have co-ordinates $(-1,0)$ and B have co-ordinates $(1,0)$. Let P be a moving point with co-ordinates (x,y). If a is the length of segment PA and b is the length of PB, find the equation of the locus of P when:

    (a) $a/b = 2$,
    (b) $a + b = 2$,
    (c) $a - b = 2$,
    (d) $a^2 + b^2 = 2$,
    (e) $a^2 - b^2 = 2$.

★8. Let P be a point on the circle $x^2 + y^2 = 1$, let Q be the point $(4,0)$, and let M be the midpoint of the segment PQ. Find the locus of point M.

★9. Fold a paper several times so that a given point falls on a given line. Do the creases appear to form a system of lines tangent to a familiar curve?

★10. Construct several equilateral triangles with one vertex at a fixed point A and with a second vertex, B, on a given line. What seems to be the locus of the third vertex C? Test your conjecture by attempting to construct an equilateral triangle having one vertex at a given point, a second vertex on a given line, and the third vertex on a given circle.

5

Elementary Transformations

~~~~~~

5.1 REFLECTION ABOUT A LINE

In elementary geometry it is assumed that a geometric figure can be moved to a new position without changing its size or shape. In proving that two triangles are congruent, one triangle may be placed so that one side coincides with the corresponding side of the second triangle. If one imagines that the first triangle is cut from cardboard, the process of making this triangle coincide with the second one may be considered to involve some combination of the operations of sliding along a line (translation), turning about a point (rotation), and turning over (reflection about a line). This chapter will be concerned with a study of properties of these and similar transformations; more general transformations will be introduced in later chapters.

Definition 1. *A **transformation** is a correspondence, or rule, that associates with every point, P, in a plane another point, P', called the **image** of P.*

Definition 2. *Let c represent a geometric configuration composed of lines (or segments), circles (or arcs), and points. If c is the locus of a point P, the image of c, called c', in a transformation, is the locus of P' the image of P in the transformation.*

This definition may be extended to include more general figures so that as a point P traces a curve, its image point P' will generate the image of the first curve.

Definition 3. *The image of a point P, under **reflection** about a given line l, is the point P' for which PP' is perpendicular to l and the segment PP' is bisected by l. If P is on l, P and P' coincide. If P is the ideal point on the line through A and B, P' is the ideal point on the line A'B'.*

69

Theorem 1. *The reflection of a straight line, about a line, is a straight line.*

Proof: When line a, Figure 39, is reflected about line l it is to be shown that a', the image of a, is also a straight line. If a is the ideal line, or if a is the line l, Definitions 3 and 2 show that a and its image a' coincide. From these definitions it also follows that the image of any line parallel to l is a second line parallel to l. If a intersects l at point Q,

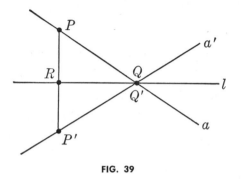

FIG. 39

Q and its image point Q' coincide. Let P be any point on a and locate its image P' in the reflection about l. Let PP' cut l at R. Triangles RPQ and $RP'Q$ are congruent, since sides including the right angles are equal. Thus angles PQR and $P'QR$ are equal, and the locus of P' is a fixed line through Q. It is also evident that as P moves along the entire line a, P' traces all of the line a'.

Theorem 2. *The length of a line segment is unchanged by reflection about a line.*

The proof is left as an exercise.

Theorem 3. *The angle between two intersecting lines is preserved under reflection about a line.*

The proof is left as an exercise. The student should show that order is reversed if directed angles are involved.

Theorem 4. *The reflection of a circle, about a line, is a circle.*

Proof: Let a circle with center O and radius r be reflected about a line. Let O' be the image of O and let P' be the image of any point P on the circumference of the first circle. From Theorem 2 it follows that $OP = O'P' = r$. Since O' and r are fixed, P' must lie on the circle with center O' and radius r. It is also evident that as P traces the first circle, P' traces an entire circle.

Theorem 5. *If c' is the image of a figure c, in a reflection about a line, c is also the image of c' in the same reflection.*

Proof: This property follows from the symmetric role of points P and P' in Definition 3.

In considering a physical interpretation of a geometric transformation, it is often convenient to think of starting with two coincident planes and moving one while keeping the second fixed. If one of two coincident planes is rotated through 180°, about a line l in the plane, the planes will again be coincident, but the old and new positions of a point on the first plane will be the same as those of a point in the second plane and its image under reflection about l. With this interpretation, the truth of the theorems of the section is apparent; the proofs were given to illustrate the procedure to be used when a simple physical interpretation is not available.

Definition 4. *Two curves, which are images of each other under reflection about a line, are said to be **symmetric** with respect to the line. A figure is said to be symmetric about a line if the image of the figure, in a reflection about the line, coincides with the figure.*

Problem 1. *Two equal circles are given. Find a reflection about a line so that each circle is the image of the other.*

Solution: Let the circles of equal radii have centers at points A and B. Each circle is the image of the other in a reflection about the line that is the perpendicular bisector of AB.

Problem 2. *Construct a line through the inaccessible intersection of two lines and through a given point.*

Solution: Let a and b be given lines whose intersection is not accessible (for example, if a and b are lines on a blackboard, the point of intersection may be above the blackboard) and let P be the given point. Reflect a, b, and P about some convenient line l so the reflected lines a' and b' intersect at Q'. The reflection of line $P'Q'$ about l produces a line through P and through the intersection of a and b.

If lines a and b are parallel, or nearly parallel, this solution is not useful, since the point Q' will also be inaccessible. Exercise 1, below, gives an elementary solution which is valid for this case.

EXERCISES

1. Prove the following method for constructing a line through a given point P and the inaccessible intersection of two given lines a and b. Let a line through P cut a and b in points A and B. Let a line parallel to AB intersect a and b in points A' and B'. Construct P' on $A'B'$ so that $AP/PB = A'P'/P'B'$. The line PP' passes through the intersection of a and b.

2. Although Definition 3 gives the image of an ideal point in the reflection about an ordinary line, it does not define the image of a point in a reflection about the ideal line. Mention possible advantages or objections to extending Definition 3 by adding that a point and its image coincide in a reflection about the ideal line.

3. Construct the image of a given ideal point in a reflection about a line. *Hint:* An ideal point may be given by showing two ordinary points and stating that the ideal point is on the line through these points.

4. What are "rigid motion" transformations?

5. In a transformation, a point is called fixed if it coincides with its own image point. Describe all fixed points in a reflection about a line.

6. How many lines exist so that a regular polygon of n sides is symmetric about each line?

5.2   REFLECTION ABOUT A POINT

Definitions of geometric figures, or transformations, may be divided into two general classes: descriptive definitions which give properties of the term defined; and constructive definitions which tell how to construct the desired figure, or image points in the case of a transformation. This chapter presents descriptive definitions of geometric transformations and the following discussions show how the corresponding images of points, lines and circles may be constructed by straightedge and compass.

When the definition of a transformation involves lengths of line segments, a special definition is needed to give the image of an ideal point. This can be simplified, in some cases, by use of the definition of a fixed point.

Definition 1. *A point is a **fixed** point in a transformation if it coincides with its own image point.*

Definition 2. *The image of a point P, under **reflection** about a given point O, is the point P' for which the segment PP' is bisected by O. All ideal points, and the point O, are fixed points in the reflection about O.*

Definition 3. *In a transformation T_1, let the image of a point P be P_1'; in a transformation T_2, let the image of P be P_2'. The transformations T_1 and T_2 are* **equivalent** *if and only if for every point P in the plane, the image points P_1' and P_2' are identical.*

Theorem 1. *Reflection about a point O is equivalent to a reflection about any line l, through O, followed by a reflection about the line l' which passes through O and is perpendicular to l.*

Proof: Let P' be the reflection of any point P, about point O, Figure 40, and let l and l' be any two perpendicular lines through O. Let the line through P, perpendicular to l, and the line through P', perpendicular

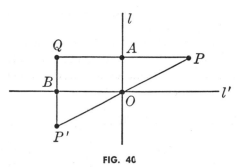

FIG. 40

to l' intersect at Q. Let l cut QP at A and let l' cut QP' at B. From the congruent triangles BOP' and APO, it follows that $PA = AQ$ and $QB = BP'$. Hence Q is the reflection of P about l and P' is the reflection of Q about l'.

Since by use of Theorem 1, a reflection about a point can be obtained by two reflections about lines, the proof that the reflection of a line about a point gives another line follows from Theorem 1 of Section 5.1. In the same manner, Theorems 1, 2, 3, 4, and 5 of § 5.1 are true if the words *about a line* are replaced by *about a point.*

Definition 4. *Two figures which are images of each other in a reflection about a point are said to be* **symmetric** *with respect to the point. A figure is said to be symmetric about a point if the image of the figure, in a reflection about the point, coincides with the figure.*

EXERCISES

1. Directly from the definition of the transformation, prove that the reflection of a circle, about a given point, is a circle.

2. Use a limit process to show that the definition given for the image of an ideal point, in a reflection about a line, is consistent with the definition of the image of an ordinary point.

3. Give necessary and sufficient conditions for a regular polygon to be symmetric with respect to a point.

4. If a figure is symmetric about each of two perpendicular lines, is it necessarily symmetric about a point?

5. Let two equal circles and a triangle be given. Find the reflection about a point in which the circles are images of each other. In this same reflection find the image of the given triangle.

6. A transformation which leaves every point in the plane fixed is called the **identity transformation.** Show that a reflection about a given line followed by a second reflection about the same line is equivalent to the identity transformation.

7. Definition 2 does not cover reflection about an ideal point. Mention possible advantages or objections to extending Definition 2 by adding that a point and its image coincide in a reflection about an ideal point.

5.3   TRANSLATION AND ROTATION

Definition 1. *The image of a point P under* **translation,** *sometimes called* **parallel displacement,** *is the point P′ for which the directed segment PP′ is parallel to and equal to a given directed segment AB. Each ideal point is a fixed point in the translation.*

In applying this definition it is understood that a positive direction is assigned to the line containing the segment AB and that the same positive direction is used on any line parallel to AB. Thus, in Definition 1, the points A, B, $P′$, and P, taken in order, are consecutive vertices of a parallelogram.

Definition 2. *The image of a point P, under* **rotation** *about a point O, is the point P′ for which PO = P′O and for which angle POP′ is equal to a given angle both in magnitude and direction; the point O is a fixed point; the image of the ideal point on the line OP is the ideal point on the line OP′.*

In both translation and rotation a simple physical interpretation, involving rigid motion, shows that a curve is congruent to its image. Hence the image of a given point, line, or circle under a given translation or rotation (or a combination of both) is again a point, line, or circle which can be constructed by ruler and compass.

In reflection about a line, or about a point, if $P′$ is the image of P, then P is also the image of $P′$ in the same reflection. In general, this property is not true for a translation or for a rotation, although it is true for a rotation through 180°.

Since a rotation of 180° about a point O is equivalent to a reflection about point O, reflection about a point is a special case of rotation.

If two directly congruent triangles are given, it is easy to find a rotation followed by a translation so that the second triangle is the image of the first in the combined transformation. For example, let triangles ABC and $A'B'C'$, Figure 41, be directly congruent. For any arbitrary point O, a rotation about O can be found so that the image of triangle ABC is a triangle $A''B''C''$, with sides parallel to the corresponding sides of triangle $A'B'C'$, and with $A''B''$ having the same direction as $A'B'$. After a translation, determined by the directed segment $A''A'$, the image of $A''B''C''$ is $A'B'C'$.

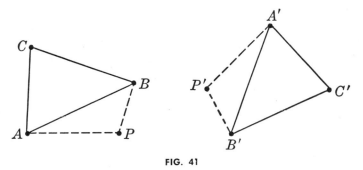

FIG. 41

Any choice of a rotation and translation for which $A'B'C'$, Figure 41, is the image of ABC will determine the same image, P', for a given point P, since triangles ABP and $A'B'P'$ must be congruent. In this sense, two directly congruent triangles determine a unique transformation, no matter what succession of rotations and translations are used to make the first coincide with the second.

EXERCISES

1. Construct a line through the inaccessible intersection of two given lines and through a given point, using translation.

2. Solve Exercise 1, using rotation.

3. Given two circles with equal radii, show that they are images in a translation.

4. Given two circles with equal radii, show that the second is the image of the first in an unlimited number of distinct rotations.

5. Line segment AB is equal to segment $A'B'$ where A, B, A', and B' are given points. If A' and B' are images of A and B in a transformation, consisting of rotations and translations, is the image of a given point P uniquely determined?

6. Let two directly congruent triangles be given. Suppose that the triangles do not have corresponding sides parallel so that the second is not the image of the first in a translation. Is there a single rotation in which the second triangle is the image of the first?

5.4 HOMOTHETIC FIGURES

Two similar geometric figures which are not congruent cannot be made to coincide by any combination of the distance preserving transformations discussed previously. In order to treat similar figures, from a transformation viewpoint, a suitable change of scale will be introduced.

Definition 1. *Let O be a given point and k be a given finite constant different from zero. The point P', on OP, for which OP'/OP = k is the image of P in an **expansion** of order k about point O. All ideal points, as well as O, are fixed points in the expansion.*

The segments OP and OP' are directed segments so that P and P' are on the same side of O when k is positive, and on opposite sides of O when k is negative. For $k = -1$, the expansion is equivalent to a reflection about the point O; for $k = 1$, the expansion is the identity transformation.

Definition 2. *A figure and its image, in an expansion of order k about point O, are said to be **homothetic**. The point O is the homothetic **center** and k is the homothetic **ratio**.*

To follow the pattern established in earlier sections of this chapter, it will be shown that the homothetic images of lines and circles are again lines and circles. It will be shown that two similar figures, with corresponding line segments parallel, determine a homothetic transformation in which one figure is the image of the second.

The literal meaning of the word *homothetic* is "placed in like position." The student may be familiar with the **pantograph,** a linkage used to enlarge or to reduce drawings, by mechanically drawing a curve homothetic to a given one.

Theorem 1. *The homothetic image of a given line is a line parallel to the given one.*

Analysis: Let the line l, the homothetic center O, and the homothetic ratio k be given; in Figure 42, k is negative. Let P be any point on l and let P' be the image of P in the given expansion. Let A be the foot of the perpendicular from O to l, with A' the image of A. To prove that the locus of P' is a line parallel to l, it is sufficient to show that angle

$OA'P'$ is a right angle. This can be accomplished by using similar triangles to show that angles $OA'P'$ and OAP are equal.

Proof: By construction $OA'/OA = OP'/OP = k$. This gives the relation $OA/OP = OA'/OP'$. Triangles $OA'P'$ and OAP are similar, since the sides including the vertical angles are proportional. It follows that angles $OA'P'$ and OAP are both right angles and that P' lies on the line through A' parallel to l.

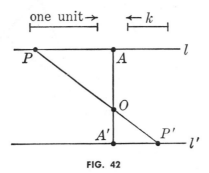

FIG. 42

From Theorem 1 it follows that the homothetic image of a line segment is a line segment. Since lengths of segments are not preserved in homothetic transformations, a statement concerning the relation between the length of a segment and the length of its image is introduced. If, in Figure 42, AP is a given segment having the homothetic image $A'P'$, it follows from similar triangles that $A'P'/AP = k$. This result is contained in Theorem 2.

Theorem 2. *If points A' and P' are images of A and P respectively, in an expansion of order k, then $A'P'/AP = k$.*

Theorem 1 shows that the homothetic image of a polygon is a second polygon with sides parallel to the corresponding sides of the first. Conversely, if two triangles have corresponding sides parallel, one is the image of the other in an expansion; the proof of Theorem 3 shows how to find the related homothetic center and the homothetic ratio.

Theorem 3. *Two triangles are homothetic if their corresponding sides are parallel.*

Plan of proof: Let triangles ABC and $A'B'C'$, Figure 43, have corresponding sides parallel and let AA' intersect BB' at O. Let the triangle $A''B''C''$ be homothetic to ABC with homothetic center O and homothetic ratio $A'B'/AB$. Then show that $A''B''C''$ coincides with $A'B'C'$.

Proof: Triangles ABC and $A'B'C'$ are similar, since corresponding angles are equal, with $A'B'/AB = B'C'/BC$. By the homothetic transformation given in the above plan, A'' must coincide with A' and B'' must coincide with B'. Since both $A''C''$ and $A'C'$ are parallel to AC and both $B''C''$ and $B'C'$ are parallel to BC, C'' and C' must coincide.

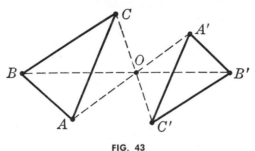

FIG. 43

The above proof is not valid if AA' and BB' meet in an ideal point. In this case, however, the triangles are congruent and triangle $A'B'C'$ is the image of ABC in the translation determined by directed segment AA'. Theorem 3 may be restated "If two triangles have corresponding sides parallel, lines joining corresponding vertices are concurrent." For the exceptional case, discussed in this paragraph, this point of concurrency is an ideal point.

Theorem 4. *A necessary and sufficient condition for two polygons to be homothetic is that all corresponding sides and diagonals of the polygons be parallel.*

The diagonals as well as the sides are included in this statement since, for example, a square and a rectangle may have corresponding sides parallel without being similar. A proof of Theorem 4 may be made by repeated applications of Theorem 3. By treating a circle as a limiting position of a regular polygon, Theorem 4 suggests that the homothetic image is a circle. A direct proof of this fact is given below.

Theorem 5. *The homothetic image of a circle is a circle.*

Proof: Let the circle with center A, Figure 44, be given and let A' be the image of A in the expansion of order k about point O. Let P be any point on the given circle and let P' be the image of P. By Theorem 2, $A'P' = k(AP)$. Since A' is a fixed point and $k(AP)$ is constant, the locus for P' is the circle with center at A' and radius $k(AP)$.

If two regular polygons with an even number of sides are homothetic, they have two distinct homothetic centers since the corresponding parallel sides may be chosen in two ways. This indicates that two given circles should also have two homothetic centers.

Theorem 6. *Two given circles are homothetic with homothetic centers at the two points in which the line of centers is divided internally and externally in the ratio of the radii.*

The proof is left as an exercise.

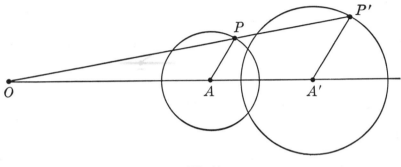

FIG. 44

EXERCISES

1. Prove that an angle is invariant in an expansion.

2. If a figure c' is the homothetic image of a figure c with homothetic center O and homothetic ratio k, describe a homothetic transformation in which c is the image of c'.

3. The sides of one square are parallel to the sides of a second square. How many homothetic centers exist?

4. Show that a common tangent to two circles passes through a homothetic center of the circles.

5. Describe the location of the homothetic centers for two circles for special cases including tangent circles and circles with equal radii.

6. A transformation consisting of rotations, translations, and expansions changes the given points A and B into the given points A' and B', respectively. Does this transformation uniquely determine the image of a point P?

5.5 HOMOTHETIC CONSTRUCTIONS

One purpose for introducing the transformations considered in this chapter was to provide a background for the study of the inversion transformation which is the central topic of Chapter 6. Elementary transformations do have numerous applications, however, in solutions of construction problems. The three problems solved below illustrate types of problems in which the homothetic transformation provides a direct solution.

Problem 1. *Given two lines l_1 and l_2 and a point P, construct a line through P cutting l_1 at A and l_2 at B so that P divides the segment AB in a given ratio.*

Analysis: In Figure 45, the given ratio is $k = m/n$. If point B moves on l_2 the locus for A, with A on BP so that $AP/PB = k$, is a line homothetic to l_2 with homothetic center at P and with homothetic ratio equal to $-k$.

Construction: Construct line l_3 which is the homothetic image of line l_2 with homothetic center P and homothetic ratio $-k$. In Figure 45, this was done by first swinging an arc with P as center and n as radius,

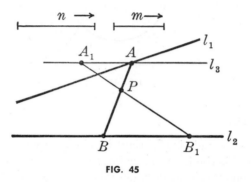

FIG. 45

cutting l_2 at B_1. Next an arc was drawn with center P and radius m, cutting B_1P at A_1, with P between A_1 and B_1. Finally through A_1, l_3 was drawn parallel to l_2. The line l_3 cuts l_1 in the desired point A and line AP determines point B on l_2.

Proof: Since A is the image of B in an expansion of order $-k$ about point P, no additional proof is needed to show that $AP/PB = k$, although a direct proof, using similar triangles, is possible.

Discussion: If l_1 and l_2 are not parallel, there is exactly one solution for any positive or negative ratio k, since lines l_3 and l_1 will intersect in one point. If the given lines are parallel, l_3 will either be parallel to l_1, so no solution exists, or else l_3 and l_1 will coincide so that every line through P is a solution.

Problem 2. *Through a point of intersection of two circles, draw a line on which the circles intercept chords having a given ratio.*

Analysis: Let the given circles, with centers A and B, intersect at P. As point Q traces the circumference of circle A its image point, Q', in the expansion about P with the given ratio, will trace another circle passing through P and homothetic to circle A. The intersection of this circle and circle B determines a second point on the desired line through P.

The construction and proof are left as exercises.

Problem 3. *In a given triangle, inscribe a triangle having sides parallel to the corresponding sides of a second triangle.*

Analysis and construction: Given triangles ABC and XYZ, Figure 46, points X'' on CA, Y'' on AB, and Z'' on BC are to be found so that the sides of triangle $X''Y''Z''$ are parallel to the corresponding sides of XYZ. Pick an arbitrary point X' on CA and locate Y' on AB so that $X'Y'$ is parallel to XY. Through X' and Y' draw lines, parallel to XZ

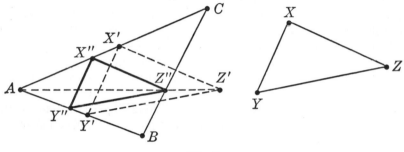

FIG. 46

and YZ, intersecting at Z'. If $X''Y''Z''$ is the desired solution, triangles $X''Y''Z''$ and $X'Y'Z'$ are homothetic, since corresponding sides are parallel, and the homothetic center must be the point A which is the intersection of line $X'X''$ and $Y'Y''$. Line AZ' locates Z'' on BC and the line through Z'' parallel to $X'Z'$ locates X'' on CA. Let the line through X'' parallel to $X'Y'$ and the line through Z'' parallel to $Y'Z'$ intersect at Y''.

Proof: From the construction, triangles $X''Y''Z''$ and XYZ have parallel sides and it is only necessary to prove that Y'' lies on AB. Since triangles $X''Y''Z''$ and $X'Y'Z'$ are homothetic with $X'X''$ and $Z'Z''$ intersecting at A, $Y'Y''$ also passes through A and Y'' is on AB.

Discussion: If vertices of $X''Y''Z''$ may also lie on the extended sides of triangle ABC, the problem has one solution since line AZ' will cut BC in one point.

Related problems: The solution of Problem 3 shows that the problem of inscribing in a given triangle a triangle similar to a second given one has an unlimited number of solutions. This suggests related problems, without suggesting methods of solution, such as the following: (*a*) In a given triangle, inscribe a triangle similar to a second given triangle with one side passing through a given point. (*b*) In a given triangle, inscribe a triangle congruent to a second given triangle. (*c*) In a given quadrilateral, inscribe a quadrilateral similar to a given one. These and similar problems will be discussed later.

EXERCISES

1. Through a point inside a circle, construct a chord which is trisected by the point.

2. Given a point P, a line l, and a circle O, find a point A on l and a point B on the circumference of O so that P bisects the segment AB. If the circle is on one side of the given line, describe the region in which P must be located for a solution to exist.

3. Solve Problem 1 of this section for the special case in which l_1 and l_2 are sides of an equilateral triangle, P is the midpoint of the third side, and the given ratio is -3.

4. In a circle, inscribe a rectangle similar to a given one.

5. In a given triangle, inscribe a square with two vertices on a given side of the triangle.

6. Construct a triangle given two lines along which two sides of the triangle lie and the centroid, which is the point of intersection of the medians.

7. Given three concurrent lines, construct a transversal so that the two segments intercepted by the given lines shall have given lengths.

5.6   COMBINED TRANSFORMATIONS

A reflection about a point O, followed by a rotation of 90° about O, is equivalent to a rotation of 270° about O. The notation $T_1 = T_2$ will be used to indicate that the two transformations T_1 and T_2 are equivalent, Definition 3 of § 5.2. It is also convenient to have a notation to indicate that points in a plane are carried into a new position by one transformation and that the new points are then moved to another position by a second transformation.

Definition 1. *If T_1 and T_2 are given point transformations, the image, P, of a point in the product transformation $T = T_2 \cdot T_1$ is obtained by first finding the image, P_1, of P in the transformation T_1 and then finding the image of P_1 in the transformation T_2.*

In each of the transformations discussed in this chapter, the image of a triangle is another triangle similar to (or congruent to) the original one. It might be asked if there are other transformations having this property. As a help in solving construction problems, no additional transformations of this type are necessary, since a product of the elementary transformations studied in this chapter can carry a given triangle into a second given triangle if it is similar to the first one.

It is said that some persons decide where to take a vacation by blindly pointing to a spot on a map. A mathematical variation consists of starting with two identical maps, placing one on a table and then dropping the second map on the first in an arbitrary manner. The one location on the second map that falls on top of the same location on the first map determines the vacation spot.

That there is, in general, a fixed point in the transformation changing the points on one map into the corresponding points on the other is proved in Theorem 1. Such a point might not be inside the boundaries of the maps, and if it were, a person with enough imagination to try this scheme might stay at home and take an imaginary vacation.

Example 1. *Using the conventional rectangular co-ordinate system, let T_1 be a translation of one unit to the left and let T_2 be a rotation of 60° counterclockwise about the origin. Find a fixed point in the product transformation $T = T_2 \cdot T_1$ and describe the equivalent single transformation T.*

Solution: In Figure 47 let P be any point, let P_1 be the image of P in the transformation T_1, let P' be the image of P_1 in the transformation T_2. Then the point Q with co-ordinates $x = \frac{1}{2}$, $y = -\frac{1}{2}\sqrt{3}$ is a fixed point in the transformation T.

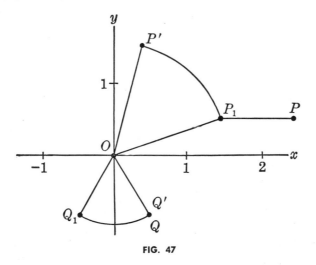

FIG. 47

The student should verify that Q is a fixed point by finding the co-ordinates of Q_1 and Q'. He should also verify that, since lengths of line segments are preserved in translations and rotations, $QP = QP'$. Also, using the fact that in a rotation of 60° the image of any given line makes an angle of 60° with the original, he should verify that $\angle PQP' = 60°$. These properties show that the transformation T is a rotation of 60°, counterclockwise, about point Q.

The above example suggests that every translation followed by a rotation is equivalent to a single rotation. If so, two points P and Q and the images P' and Q' are sufficient to determine the transformation, since the center of rotation lies on the perpendicular bisectors of segments PP' and QQ'. Theorem 1 contains a still more general result.

Theorem 1. *A given line segment can be transformed into a second given segment by a rotation and an expansion about the same point.*

Proof: In Figure 48, A, B, A', and B' are given points. In a transformation to be found, A' and B' are images of A and B respectively.

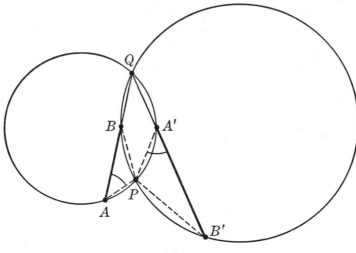

FIG. 48

If AB and $A'B'$ are parallel, an expansion about the intersection of lines AA' and BB' is sufficient.

Let AB and $A'B'$ meet at the finite point Q, Figure 48. Let the circle through points A, A', and Q, and the circle through B, B', and Q, intersect at point P.

To show that segment AB may be carried into $A'B'$ by a rotation and an expansion about P, it is sufficient to show that triangles ABP and $A'B'P$ are directly similar. These triangles are similar, since angles BAP and $B'A'P$ are both measured by one-half of arc $PA'Q$ and angles ABP and $A'B'P$ are measured by one-half of arc PBQ.

Consider any of the transformations discussed in this chapter or a product of such transformations. If a point traces any rectilinear figure, the image point, in this transformation, must trace a similar (or congruent) figure. As a point traces a path, not necessarily a line or a circle, the image point will be said to trace a similar path.

Theorem 2. *If a variable triangle remains similar to a given triangle, if one vertex remains fixed, and if a second vertex traces a geometric configuration, then the third vertex traces a similar configuration.*

Proof: Let the variable triangle ABC have A as a fixed vertex. For any position of ABC let T_1 be an expansion about A of order k, where $k = AC/AB$. Let T_2 be a rotation, through angle BAC, about point A. Then in the transformation $T = T_1 \cdot T_2$ vertex C is the image of vertex B for every position of triangle ABC. Hence the locus of C must be the image of the locus of B in the transformation T.

Theorem 3. *Let a variable polygon undergo simultaneous rotation and expansion about a fixed point in such a way that the polygon remains similar to a given polygon and one vertex traces a geometric figure. Then each vertex will trace a similar geometric figure.*

Proof: Theorem 2 may be applied by considering the triangle determined by the fixed point, the vertex of the polygon which traces the geometric figure, and an arbitrary vertex of the polygon.

EXERCISES

1. If T_1 is a translation and T_2 is a rotation, does $T_1 \cdot T_2 = T_2 \cdot T_1$?

2. Solve Exercise 10 of the review exercises of § 4.3, using Theorem 2 of the present section.

3. In a given triangle inscribe a triangle, similar to a second given one, with one vertex at a fixed point on one side of the first triangle.

4. Construct an equilateral triangle with one vertex at a given point and with the other vertices on two given circles.

5. Construct a triangle, similar to a given one, with each vertex on a different one of three given circles. How many solutions are possible?

6. Inscribe a triangle, similar to a given one, in a given circle.

7. Let ABC and $A'B'C'$ be two directly congruent triangles. Are the perpendicular bisectors of the segments AA', BB', and CC' concurrent?

REVIEW EXERCISES

1. For each transformation considered in this chapter, let I be the ideal point on a given line and construct a line through a given point and through I', the image of I in the transformation.

2. Join the midpoints of the sides of a triangle to form a second triangle. Find a homothetic transformation in which the second triangle is the image of the first.

3. Find an English word, containing more than three letters, which reads the same from both sides of a window on which it is printed in capital letters. Consider both horizontal and vertical arrangements.

4. In a given circular sector, inscribe a square (a) with two vertices on one radius, (b) with two vertices on the circular arc.

5. Construct a line through a given point so that the two segments determined on the line by three given concurrent lines shall be equal.

6. Perpendicular bisectors of segments AA', BB', and CC' are concurrent. Are the triangles ABC and $A'B'C'$ necessarily congruent?

7. Let P be any point on the circumference of the circle whose diameter is the line segment joining the homothetic centers of two given circles. Show that one circle is the image of the other in a rotation and an expansion about P.

8. Review each transformation introduced in this chapter by explaining how it may be used to construct a line through the inaccessible intersection of two given lines and through a given point.

★9. Show that any translation is the product of two reflections about lines.

★10. Given a point P with rectangular co-ordinates (x,y), find the co-ordinates of the image point P' under (a) reflection about the x-axis, (b) reflection about the origin, (c) translation in which $(0,0)$ becomes (x_1,y_1), (d) rotation through angle θ about the origin, (e) expansion of order k about the origin.

★11. Solve Exercise 10 using polar co-ordinates.

★12. Find the equation of the image of the curve

$$a(x^2 + y^2) + bx + cy + d = 0$$

under expansion about the origin. Use this result to prove Theorems 1 and 5 of section 5.4.

★13. Discuss the construction of the pantograph, a linkage for drawing a curve homothetic to a given one.

6

Inversion

~~~~~~

6.1 INVERSE POINTS

In each transformation considered in Chapter 5 the image of a point, line, or circle is again a point, line, or circle, respectively. If the primary interest in transformations is that the image of a figure composed of points, lines, and circles be another figure composed of points, lines, and circles, other transformations, such as one which changes points to lines and lines to points, may be introduced. In the inversion, transformation images of lines may be either lines or circles and images of circles may also be either lines or circles.

Definition 1. *The point P' is the image of point P, in an inversion of modulus k with respect to a fixed point O if, P' is on OP and if $OP \cdot OP' = k$. The image of point O is the ideal line and conversely.*

The line segments in Definition 1 are directed segments so that P and P' are on the same side of O for k positive and on opposite sides of O for k negative. The point O is called the ***center of inversion*** and $\sqrt{k}$ is called the ***radius of inversion.*** If k is positive, the circle with center O and radius $\sqrt{k}$ is called the ***circle of inversion.***

If P' is the image of P in an inversion, it follows directly from Definition 1 that P is also the image of P' in the same inversion. If P' is the image of a point P in an inversion of modulus k with respect to O, and if P'' is the image of P in an inversion of modulus $-k$ with respect to O, then P' and P'' are images in a reflection about the point O. For this reason, the following discussion will be limited to the case in which k is positive.

Problem 1. *Construct the image of a point in a given inversion.*

First solution: Let the circle of inversion and a point P be given. If the circle of inversion has center O and radius r, so that r^2 is the modulus of inversion, then $OP' = r^2/OP$ and the segment OP' may be constructed as the fourth proportional to three given segments, Problem 5 of § 1.9.

Second solution: Let O be the circle of inversion, Figure 49. If P lies outside the circle, construct a line through P tangent to the circle at T. The perpendicular from T to OP cuts OP at P', the image point of P. This is proved using the similar right triangles $OP'T$ and OTP. Since $OP'/OT = OT/OP$, it follows that $OP \cdot OP' = (OT)^2 = r^2$.

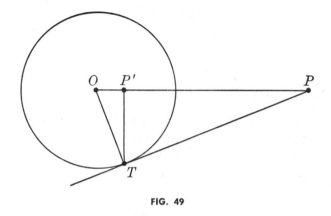

FIG. 49

If P is inside the circle of inversion, let a line perpendicular to OP at P determine a point T on the circle of inversion. The tangent to the circle of inversion at T cuts OP at P'. When P is on the circle of inversion, P and P' coincide.

EXERCISES

1. Let P be a point outside the circle of inversion with center O. Show that P', the image of P, can be constructed without the use of a straightedge, in the following manner. With P as center and OP as radius, describe an arc cutting the circle of inversion at R and S. With R and S as centers, and with radius OR, construct two arcs intersecting at P'.

2. The point P_2 bisects the segment OP_1. In an inversion of arbitrary modulus with respect to point O, does P_1' bisect the segment OP_2'?

3. In a given inversion, construct the images of several points on a line not through the center of inversion. What seems to be the locus of these inverse points?

4. What is the inverse of the circle of inversion?

5. In a given inversion, what is the inverse of a circle concentric with the circle of inversion?

6.2 INVERSE CURVES

Theorems to be proved in this section contain information concerning the images of lines and circles in the inversion transformation. Definition 1, § 6.1, states that the center of inversion has the entire ideal line as its image. In finding the image of a curve, which passes through the center of inversion, it is desirable to modify this definition to limit the image of the center of inversion to a single ideal point.

Definition 1. *Let line OA be tangent to a curve c at point O and let c' be the image of c in an inversion of arbitrary modulus with respect to point O. The ideal point on OA is the image of O which lies on the inverse curve c'.*

The image of a curve will contain an ideal point if and only if the original curve passes through the center of inversion. If, as stated in § 6.1 without proof, the image of a line (or of a circle) must be a line or a circle, the student can anticipate the theorems to be proved below. On this assumption, the image of a line (or of a circle) passing through the center of inversion contains an ideal point and must, therefore, be a line. Likewise, from this assumption, it follows that the image of a line (or circle) not through the center of inversion must be a circle.

Theorem 1. *The inverse of a straight line, through the center of inversion, is the same straight line.*

Proof: The proof follows directly from Definition 1, § 6.1, since the image of every point on the line lies on the line, and every point on the line is the image of a point on the line. That the ideal point on the line is the image of the center of inversion follows from a limiting case of Definition 1 of this section.

Theorem 2. *The inverse of a straight line not through the center of inversion is a circle through the center of inversion and, conversely, the inverse of a circle through the center of inversion is a straight line not through the center of inversion.*

Proof: In Figure 50, O is the center of the circle of inversion. If line l, not through O, is given, let the perpendicular from O cut l at A. Let A' be the image of A in the given inversion. If P is an arbitrary point on l, it will be shown that the corresponding image point, P', lies on the circle having OA' as diameter. By the definition of inverse points, $OA \cdot OA' = OP \cdot OP' = r^2$, so that $OA/OP = OP'/OA'$. Since triangles AOP and $P'OA'$ have a common angle, it follows that these triangles are similar with $\angle OP'A' = \angle OAP = 90°$. Therefore P' must lie on the circle with OA' as diameter by Theorem 1, § 4.1. The image of the ideal point on line l is the point O, Definition 1 of § 6.1.

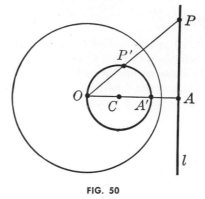

FIG. 50

Conversely, let a given circle with center C, Figure 50, pass through O, the center of the circle of inversion. Let OC cut the given circle at A'. Let point A be the image of A' in the given inversion and let l be the line through A perpendicular to OC. Let P' be any point on the given circle and let P be the corresponding image point. As in the last paragraph, it follows that triangles AOP and $P'OA'$ are similar and that $\angle OAP = \angle OP'A' = 90°$. Hence P, the image of an arbitrary point on circle C, must lie on the line l. By Definition 1 of the present section, the image of O, which lies on the inverse curve of the circle C, is the ideal point on line l.

Theorem 3. *The inverse of a circle not through the center of inversion is a circle not through the center of inversion.*

Analysis: It will be shown that a circle not through the center of inversion and its inverse curve are homothetic figures, with the center of inversion as homothetic center.

Proof: Let O be the center of the inversion of modulus k and let P be an arbitrary point on the given circle, Figure 51. Let OP cut the

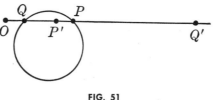

FIG. 51

circle in the second point Q and let P' and Q' be the image points of P and Q in the given inversion. By the definition of inverse points, it follows that $OP \cdot OP' = OQ \cdot OQ' = k$. Hence $OQ = k/OQ'$.

The product $OP \cdot OQ$ is a constant for every position of P on the given circle, Theorem 3 of § 2.4. If $OP \cdot OQ = m$, it follows that $OQ = m/OP$. The two expressions for OQ yield $OQ'/OP = k/m$, and by Definition 1, § 5.4, it follows that Q' is the image of P in an expansion of order k/m about point O. Hence as P traces the given circle, Q' traces a circle homothetic to the given one.

Problem 1. *Find the inversion in which a given line and a given circle are inverse curves.*

Solution: In Figure 50, let l be the given line and let C be the center of the given circle. Drop a perpendicular from C cutting l at point A. Let this line cut the given circle in points O and A' with A and A' on the same side of O. The desired circle of inversion has its center at O and its radius is the mean proportional between segments OA' and OA.

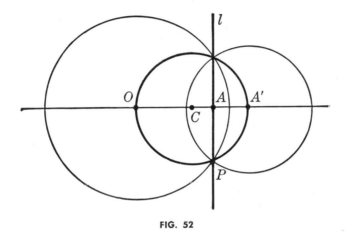

FIG. 52

Discussion: There is only one solution when l does not cut circle C or when l is tangent to circle C. If l cuts circle C, there are two real circles of inversion in which l and C are inverse curves. In Figure 52, line l and circle C intersect at P. Using the notation in the above solution for points O, A, and A', one circle of inversion has center O and radius OP. The second circle of inversion has center A' and radius $A'P$.

EXERCISES

1. Let c' be the inverse of a geometric figure c in an inversion of modulus k_1 with respect to point O. Let c'' be the inverse of c with modulus k_2 with respect to point O. Prove that c' and c'' are homothetic and find a homothetic center and ratio.

2. Why is it impossible for all points on a parabola to be inverted into points on a circle?

3. What is the inverse configuration of two parallel lines if the center of inversion is (or is not) on one of the lines? What is the inverse of a family of parallel lines?

4. What is the inverse of two tangent circles for different positions of the center of inversion?

5. Make a sketch of the configuration obtained by the inversion of a family of concentric circles.

6. Construct a real circle of inversion so that two given circles will be images of each other in the inversion transformation. Consider cases in which one circle is inside the other; the circles intersect; and the circles are mutually external. Also discuss special cases such as equal circles, tangent circles, and concentric circles.

6.3   THE PROBLEM OF APOLLONIUS, SPECIAL CASES

One of the most famous problems of Euclidean plane geometry is the *Apollonian Problem* of constructing a circle which is tangent to each one of three given circles.

If a point is considered as a limiting case of a circle with zero radius, and a line is considered the limiting case of a circle with unlimited radius, the problem of Apollonius may be considered to consist of ten special cases in which the three given elements are points, lines, and circles in some combination.

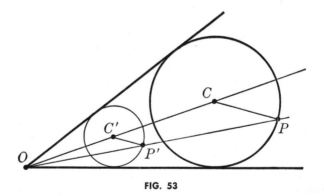

FIG. 53

A general solution for the problem of Apollonius, based on the inversion transformation, is contained in § 6.4. In the present section, special cases of the problem are solved by methods that do not require inversion. The notation (P, L, C) is used to designate the problem of constructing a circle through a given point, tangent to a given line, and tangent to a given circle. The problems (P, P, P) and (L, L, L) are familiar from elementary geometry, and the problem (P, P, L) has been discussed previously, Problem 1, § 3.2.

Problem 1. *Construct a circle tangent to two given lines and passing through a given point.*

Analysis: In Figure 53, let P be the given point and let the given lines intersect at O. The center, C, of the desired solution must be on the bisector of the proper angle at O. Let C' be any point on this bisector and construct the circle, with center at C', tangent to the two given lines. The circles with centers at C' and C are homothetic with homothetic center O, Theorem 6 of § 5.4. Hence C can be located by determining a suitable homothetic ratio. One way to do this is to draw OP and let OP cut circle C' at point P'. The line through P parallel to $P'C'$ will locate C on the bisector of the angle at O. The problem has two solutions found by letting P' be either point in which OP cuts circle C'. Further details of construction and proof are left for the student.

Each of the ten possible cases of the problem of Apollonius may also be broken down into additional classifications by considering special relations which may exist between the given elements. The solution of Problem 1 is not valid if the two given lines are parallel; Problem 2 contains a generalization of this special case.

Problem 2. *Construct a circle tangent to each of two given parallel lines and tangent to a given circle.*

Analysis: In Figure 54, l_1 and l_2 are given parallel lines and the given circle has center O and radius r. One locus for the center of a solution

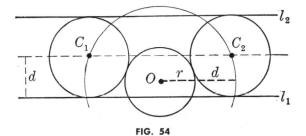

FIG. 54

circle is the line midway between the parallel lines. A second locus for the center is the circle with center O and radius $r + d$, where d is half of the distance between the parallel lines. In Figure 54, C_1 and C_2 are centers of two solution circles.

The number of solutions may vary from zero to four depending on the positions of the given circle and lines. For example, if circle O cuts both l_1 and l_2, the center of a solution circle may lie on a circle with center O and radius $r - d$.

Problem 3. *Construct a circle tangent to each of three given circles having equal radii.*

Analysis: Let each of the circles, with centers at A, B, and C, Figure 55, have radius r. Let O be the point of intersection of perpendicular bisectors of AB and BC. Then O is the center of the circle through points A, B, and C. If O is outside each given circle, the circle with center O and radius $OA - r$ is externally tangent to each given circle. The circle with center O and radius $OA + r$ is internally tangent to each given circle.

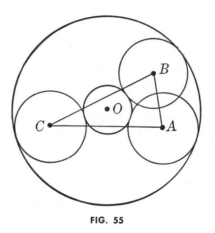

FIG. 55

Number of solutions: If the given equal circles are mutually external, with centers not collinear, the above analysis provides two solutions. Additional solutions exist and may be found by methods of the following section.

EXERCISES

1. Construct all circles tangent to three given lines.

2. Can the problem of constructing a line tangent to two given circles be considered as a special case of the problem of Apollonius?

3. Let three given circles, with equal radii, have centers on the same line. Can the solution given for Problem 3 be used to find a circle tangent to these three circles?

4. Why does one not give a straightforward solution of the problem of Apollonius by neglecting one of the three given circles and finding the locus of centers of all circles tangent to the other two circles?

5. Construct a circle tangent to three given lines by the following method. Start with a convenient circle and draw lines parallel to the

given lines and tangent to the chosen circle. The circle and its tangent lines are homothetic to the given lines and a solution circle. Can this method give four distinct solutions?

6.4 THE PROBLEM OF APOLLONIUS, GENERAL SOLUTION

Let two given circles be tangent to each other at a point T. If T is used as a center of inversion, with an arbitrary radius of inversion, the given circles invert into two lines, Theorem 2 of § 6.2. These lines must be parallel, since the image of T, which is an ideal point, is the only point on both lines.

Likewise, if two tangent circles are inverted with respect to a circle of inversion not on either circle the images are again two tangent circles. Finally, if two tangent circles are inverted with respect to a center of inversion on the circumference of only one of the circles, the inverse figures are a circle and a line tangent to this circle.

The inversion transformation may be applied to the solution of certain types of construction problem by: (a) inversion of the given configuration; (b) making a construction, using elements of the image of the original configuration; (c) another inversion, using the original circle of inversion, to place constructed elements into proper relation with respect to the given data.

As an illustration of the use of inversion, Problem 1 of § 6.3 will now be solved by a second method.

Problem 1. *Construct a circle tangent to two given lines and passing through a given point.*

Analysis: In Figure 56, P is the given point and the given lines are a and b. Assume that the circle to be constructed is tangent to lines a and b at points A and B respectively. If P is used as a center of inversion, with arbitrary modulus, the circle through A, B, and P becomes a straight line tangent to the two circles which are images of lines a and b. Construction of a line tangent to the inverse circles of lines a and b will, upon re-inversion, give a solution.

Construction: With P as center and with any convenient radius, draw a circle of inversion. Construct the images of lines a and b, which, in Figure 56, are circles with centers at R and S. Construct the line t tangent to circles R and S at A' and B'. Let PA' cut a at A and let PB' cut b at B. Since A and B are the images of A' and B' in the inversion with center at P, the circle through points A, B, and P is tangent to lines a and b.

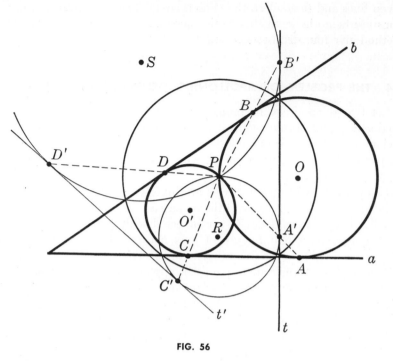

FIG. 56

There are two solutions which may be obtained from the two external tangents to the intersecting circles with centers at R and S.

Problem 2. *Construct a circle tangent to two given circles and passing through a given point.*

Discussion: The method used in Problem 1 needs only slight modifications; if the given circles are mutually external, four solutions exist since after inversion, with the given point as center of the circle of inversion, the inverse circles have four common tangents. Details are left for the student.

Problem 3. *Construct a circle tangent to three given circles.*

Discussion: The problem will be solved by changing it to an equivalent problem which has been discussed earlier. In particular it will be shown that the problem may be solved by a reduction either to Problem 2 of § 6.3 or to Problem 2 of the present section. The student should illustrate the statements made below by suitable sketches.

First analysis: Let circles with centers A, B, and C and with radii a, b, and c be given. Assume that circle A has the smallest radius. Draw the circle with center at B and with radius $b - a$, and draw the circle with center at C and with radius $c - a$. Now, Problem 2 above, construct a circle through A tangent externally to the two new circles. If the last circle has center R and radius r, the circle with center R and radius $r - a$ must be externally tangent to each of circles A, B, and C.

The student should suggest modifications to give a circle internally tangent to the three given circles. To construct a circle externally tangent to circles A and C but internally tangent to circle B, one may first construct a circle through point A, tangent to the circle with center B and radius $b + a$, and also tangent to the circle with center at C and radius $c - a$.

Second analysis: Construct three new circles, concentric with the given ones, by adding a constant, say k, to each radius so that two of the new circles are tangent at a point T. Using T as a center of inversion, this configuration is changed into one circle and two parallel lines. As in Problem 2, § 6.3, construct the two circles tangent to the lines and to the circle. After re-inversion, these circles have their radii either increased or decreased by the amount k to provide two solutions for the original problem.

Number of solutions: A complete discussion of special cases, with the corresponding number of solutions, seems too involved to present here. If the given circles are mutually external, eight solutions exist. These solutions may or may not coincide with the eight possible combinations

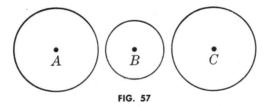

FIG. 57

of internal or external tangency. For example, in Figure 57, it should be obvious that no circle can be internally tangent to each of circles A, B, and C. The student may, however, sketch the approximate location of eight solution circles, including two which are externally tangent to all three given circles.

EXERCISES

1. Explain a method for changing the construction of a circle tangent to two given lines and also tangent to a given circle into Problem 1 of this section.

2. Start with three given circles and sketch a particular circle which seems to be tangent internally to one circle and tangent externally to the other two. Now devise a method for constructing this particular circle.

3. Three given circles intersect in the same point. How many circles are there tangent to these given circles? Describe the configuration obtained by inverting these circles with respect to a circle whose center is the common point on the circles.

4. Use inversion to construct a circle which passes through two given points and is tangent to a given line.

5. Use inversion to construct a line through a given point and through the inaccessible intersection of two given lines.

6.5   ORTHOGONAL CIRCLES

Since two tangent circles may be considered as circles which intersect at zero degrees (or at 180°), the problem of constructing a circle which intersects three given circles in three specified angles is a generalization of the problem of Apollonius. The present section contains a preliminary discussion related to several special cases of this generalization; the problem is treated in more detail in Chapter 9.

Definition 1. *The angle between two intersecting circles is the smaller of the two angles formed by the lines tangent to the circles at a point of intersection, or is a right angle if these tangents are perpendicular.*

If the circles are tangent, the angle of intersection is said to be zero degrees; otherwise the numerical value of the angle of intersection, when expressed in degrees, is a positive number no greater than 90.

Theorem 1. *The angles between two intersecting circles are the same at both points of intersection.*

The proof of Theorem 1 is left as an exercise for the student. It should also be noted that, by limiting cases of Definition 1 and Theorem 1, a line meets a circle in the same angle at both points of intersection.

Definition 2. *Two circles which intersect at right angles are said to be* **orthogonal.**

Theorem 2. *Two circles are orthogonal if and only if the tangent to each circle, at a point of intersection, passes through the center of the other circle.*

Proof: In Figure 58 the orthogonal circles with centers at A and B intersect at point T so that TR and TS are perpendicular tangents. Since both the radius TA and the line TR are perpendicular to TS, it follows that TR and TA coincide and TR must pass through A. Likewise, TS must pass through B.

Conversely, if the tangents at T do pass through the centers A and B, the tangent TS coincides with the radius TB and TB is perpendicular to the tangent TR. Hence the tangents intersect at right angles and the circles are orthogonal.

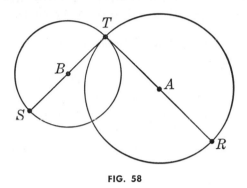

FIG. 58

Theorem 3. *Two circles are orthogonal if and only if a diameter of one, which intersects the other, cuts it in inverse points with respect to the first circle.*

Proof: In Figure 59, let the circles with centers at O and Q be orthogonal and let a line through O cut circle Q in points C and D. If P is one point of intersection of the circles, OP is tangent to circle Q and

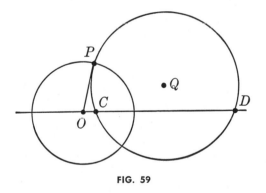

FIG. 59

$(OP)^2 = OC \cdot OD$, by Theorem 2 of § 2.2. Hence C and D are inverse points with respect to circle O.

Conversely, assume every line through O which cuts Q, cuts Q in points which are inverse with respect to circle O. Since any point on the circle of inversion is its own inverse, if circles O and Q intersect at P, line OP cuts Q in only one point, P. Therefore OP is tangent to circle Q and it follows that circles O and Q are orthogonal.

Problem 1. *Construct a circle through two given points orthogonal to a given circle.*

Analysis: Let O be the given circle and let A and B be the given points. Let A' be the inverse of A with respect to circle O. The circle through A, A', and B is orthogonal to the given circle.

Problem 2. *Through a given point construct a line which meets a given circle in a given angle.*

Analysis: Let circle O, point P, and angle A be given, Figure 60. At any point on the circumference of circle O, construct a chord, RS, meeting the tangent at R in the given angle A. Let T be the midpoint of RS and draw the circle with center O and radius OT. A line through P tangent to this circle will cut circle O in the given angle.

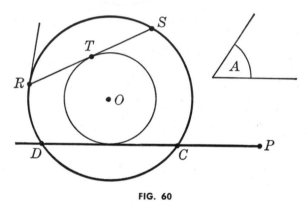

FIG. 60

Proof: Let the line from P, tangent to the circle with radius OT, cut circle O in points C and D. It remains to show that the angle between CD and the tangent to circle O at point C is equal to the given angle A. This angle is measured by one-half of arc CD. Since chords equidistant from the center of a circle are equal, and since equal chords of a circle intercept equal arcs, it follows that arcs CD and RS are equal. By construction, arc RS is numerically equal to twice angle A and, therefore, the line PC cuts circle O in the given angle.

Number of solutions: There are two solutions if P is outside the circle with center O and radius OT; if P is on this circle there is only one solution; if P is inside this circle, no solution is possible.

Problem 3. *Construct a line meeting two given circles in two given angles.*

Analysis: Given circles O and O' and angles A and B, a line is to be constructed cutting circle O in angle A and cutting circle O' in angle B.

As in Problem 2, construct circles, concentric with O and O', so that a line tangent to a new circle will cut the original circle in the desired angle. Since a line tangent to both new circles will give a solution, as many as four solutions are possible.

EXERCISES

1. Construct a circle, with a given center, orthogonal to a given circle.
2. Construct a circle passing through a given point and orthogonal to each of two given intersecting lines.
3. Construct a circle with its center on a given line, passing through a given point, and orthogonal to a given circle.
4. Through a given point construct a circle with a given radius cutting a given circle orthogonally.
5. Construct a circle, with a given center, cutting a given circle at a given angle.

6.6   INVARIANT PROPERTIES

Properties which are unchanged occupy a central position in the study of a transformation. It was noted, in § 6.4, that tangent circles remain tangent circles in an inversion transformation; this is a special case of the important property that the angle between two intersecting curves is not changed in an inversion.

Theorem 1. *The angle between two intersecting curves is invariant under inversion.*

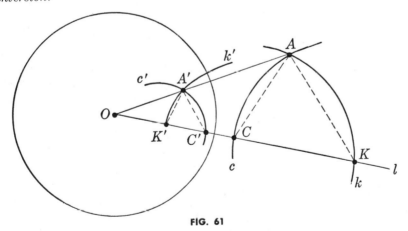

FIG. 61

Analysis: In Figure 61, let c and k be given curves intersecting at A. Let the inverse curves, with respect to the circle with center O, be the curves c' and k' intersecting at A'. Let an arbitrary line, l, through O cut curves c and k at points C and K and let C' and K' be the corresponding inverse points on c' and k'.

As line l rotates about O and approaches OA as a limiting position, it is sufficient to show that the limiting value of angle KAC is equal to the limiting value of angle $K'A'C'$. These limiting values are equal, since for every position of l, $\angle KAC = \angle K'A'C'$. The proof is completed when this equality is demonstrated.

Proof: Since quadrilaterals $A'ACC'$ and $A'AKK'$ are cyclic, Theorem 3 of § 2.4, it follows that $\angle OK'A' = \angle OAK$ and $\angle OC'A' = \angle OAC$. Hence, using Theorem 2 of § 1.5,

$$\angle K'A'C' = \angle OK'A' - \angle OC'A' = \angle OAK - \angle OAC = \angle KAC.$$

Remark: For a directed angle, inversion preserves the magnitude but reverses the direction.

Problem 1. *Through a given point construct a circle which cuts two given circles in given angles.*

Analysis: If P is the given point, invert the given elements with respect to a circle with center P and arbitrary radius. The original problem is thus changed to Problem 3 of § 6.5. Construction of a line meeting the two inverse circles in the given angles, followed by a re-inversion, gives one of the four possible solutions.

Let curves c and k be images of each other in an inversion with respect to circle O. Let c', k', and O' be the inverses of curves c, k, and O, under inversion with respect to an arbitrary circle of inversion. Are the curves c' and k' inverse curves with respect to circle O'? This question is answered by Theorem 4. Theorems 2 and 3, which are corollaries of Theorem 3, § 6.5, are stated without proofs.

Theorem 2. *A circle orthogonal to the circle of inversion inverts into itself; a circle, other than the circle of inversion, which inverts into itself is orthogonal to the circle of inversion.*

Theorem 3. *If two intersecting circles are orthogonal to the circle of inversion, they intersect in inverse points.*

Theorem 4. *Inverseness is invariant under inversion.*

Proof: In Figure 62, let A and B be any pair of points which are inverse with respect to the given circle O. Let an arbitrary inversion carry circle O into circle O' and also carry points A and B into points A' and B'. To prove the theorem, it is sufficient to show that A' and B' are images in the inversion with respect to circle O'.

Let C_1 and C_2 be any two circles through A and B. By Theorem 3, § 6.5, circles C_1 and C_2 are orthogonal to circle O. In the inversion carrying circle O into circle O', circles C_1 and C_2 become circles C_1' and C_2' orthogonal to circle O', by Theorem 1. Since circles C_1' and C_2' must intersect at A' and B', Theorem 3 shows that A' and B' are inverse points with respect to circle O'.

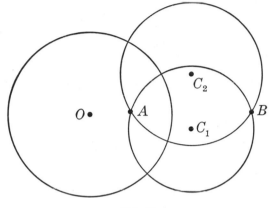

FIG. 62

Let circles A and B be inverse circles under inversion with respect to circle O. If a point on the circumference of circle O is now used as a center of inversion, circle O inverts into a straight line. Use of Theorem 4 shows that circles A' and B', which are images of A and B, are now inverse curves with respect to a straight line. In this limiting case, inversion is equivalent to reflection about a line so that A' and B' are equal circles.

A real circle of inversion, with respect to which two circles are inverse circles, is called a *circle of antisimilitude* of the circles. For any two given circles it can be proved that at least one circle of antisimilitude exists (compare Exercise 6, § 6.2). Three given circles can be inverted into equal circles by using a point of intersection of two circles of antisimilitude as the center of inversion; this provides an alternate method for obtaining a solution of the problem of Apollonius.

EXERCISES

1. The two families of lines forming the rectangular co-ordinate system are inverted with respect to a unit circle with center at the origin. Describe the resulting configuration.

2. Discuss the configuration obtained by inversion of the families of curves forming the polar co-ordinate system.

3. Invert the line segments forming the sides of an equilateral triangle, using the circumcircle of the triangle as the circle of inversion, and note the reversal in direction of angles.

4. Construct a circle passing through a given point and orthogonal to two given circles.

5. Construct a circle passing through a given point, tangent to one given circle, and orthogonal to a second given circle.

6. Given two circles, find a circle of inversion so that the first circle remains unchanged while the inverse of the second circle is a line having a given direction.

7. Show that three given circles may be inverted into circles with collinear centers by choosing a center of inversion on the circumference of the circle orthogonal to the given circles.

6.7   ADDITIONAL PROPERTIES OF INVERSION

The configuration consisting of a line passing through the center of a circle may be inverted into two orthogonal circles. Since the line passes through the center of the first circle but neither of the inverse circles passes through the center of the other, this example shows that the center of a circle does not necessarily invert into the center of the inverse circle. The following discussion is motivated by the desire to find how the inverse of the center of a circle is related to the inverse circle.

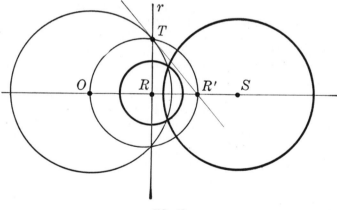

FIG. 63

In Figure 63, let the circles with centers R and S be inverse circles with respect to the circle with center O. It is easy to construct R', the inverse of R (Problem 1, § 6.1), and to note that R' does not coincide with S. Since line r, perpendicular to RS at R, and circle R are orthogonal, the inverse of r is a circle orthogonal to circle S; the inverse of r must pass through both O, Theorem 2 of § 6.2, and through R', since R is on r. Since the line $ORR'S$ cuts a circle orthogonal to circle S in points O and R', points O and R' are inverse points with respect to circle S (Theorem 3, § 6.5). This result is summarized in Theorem 1.

Theorem 1. *For two inverse circles, the inverse of the center of either circle is the inverse of the center of inversion with respect to the other circle.*

Theorem 2. *If A' and B' are inverse points of A and B with respect to a circle with center O and radius r, then*

$$A'B' = \frac{AB \cdot r^2}{OA \cdot OB}.$$

Proof: Since, in Figure 64, $OA' \cdot OA = OB \cdot OB' = r^2$, it follows that

$$\frac{OA'}{OB'} = \frac{OB}{OA}$$

so that triangles $OA'B'$ and OBA are similar. Hence

$$\frac{A'B'}{AB} = \frac{OA'}{OB} = \frac{OA' \cdot OA}{OB \cdot OA}.$$

This gives the result

$$A'B' = \frac{AB \cdot r^2}{OA \cdot OB}.$$

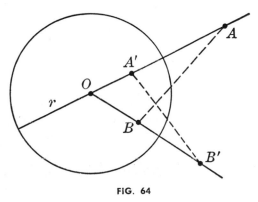

FIG. 64

The proof of Theorem 2 did not involve directed segments and the proof is not valid for the special case in which points O, A, and B are collinear. The theorem is valid in this case, however, since

$$A'B' = A'O + OB' = \frac{r^2}{AO} + \frac{r^2}{OB} = \frac{r^2(OB + AO)}{AO \cdot OB} = \frac{AB \cdot r^2}{AO \cdot OB}.$$

Although most of the applications of inversion considered in this book deal with construction problems, in which a configuration is changed into a new but related form by inversion, it is also possible to use inversion to find a theorem related to a known one. This method is used to derive the relation in Theorem 3, below. Theorem 3 is known as *Ptolemy's Theorem* and is contained in the *Almagest*, a famous astronomy book written in Egypt by Claudius Ptolemy about 150 A.D.

Theorem 3. *The vertices of a convex quadrilateral are concyclic if and only if the sum of the products of the two pairs of opposite sides is equal to the product of the diagonals.*

Proof: Let A, B, C, and D be consecutive vertices of a convex quadrilateral inscribed in a circle, Figure 65. After inversion with respect to a

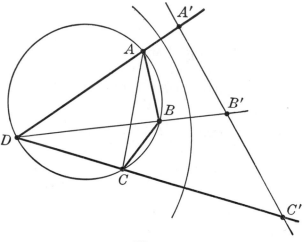

FIG. 65

circle with center at D, the inverse points A', B', and C' are collinear. Since $A'B' + B'C' = A'C'$, use of Theorem 2 gives

$$\frac{AB \cdot r^2}{DA \cdot DB} + \frac{BC \cdot r^2}{DB \cdot DC} = \frac{AC \cdot r^2}{DA \cdot DC}.$$

Clearing of fractions gives $AB \cdot CD + BC \cdot AD = AC \cdot BD$ as a necessary condition for points A, B, C, and D to be concyclic. The steps may be reversed to show that this condition is sufficient also.

The inversion transformation may, of course, be used in combination with the elementary transformations introduced in Chapter 5. It has already been mentioned that a homothetic transformation may be expressed as the product of two inversions, Exercise 1, § 6.2; reflection about a line is a special case of inversion, § 6.6; inversion with a negative modulus is equivalent to inversion with a positive modulus followed by reflection about a point, § 6.1.

Any translation is the product of two reflections about lines, see Review

Exercise 9, § 5.6. Indeed, reflection about a line l_1 followed by a reflection about a line l_2, which is parallel to l_1, is equivalent to a translation in a direction perpendicular to l_1 through a distance of twice the distance from line l_1 to line l_2.

From the above discussion it follows that a transformation which is a product of reflections, translations, rotations, and inversions is equivalent to a product transformation composed of rotations and inversions only.

EXERCISES

1. Apply Ptolemy's Theorem to a rectangle to derive the Theorem of Pythagoras.

2. An angle is inscribed in a semicircle. Describe the resulting configuration after an inversion with center at one end of the diameter.

3. A circle with center P and radius 4 is inverted with respect to a circle with center O and radius 2. If OP is 5, find the radius of the inverse circle.

4. Use only rotation and inversion to transform a given line segment AB into a second given segment $A'B'$.

5. A given circle, with center O, and a given line tangent to the given circle are inverse curves. In this inversion describe the location of O', the image of point O.

REVIEW EXERCISES

1. A configuration consisting of a circle inscribed in a triangle is inverted with one point of contact of the circle and a side as the center of inversion. Sketch the inverse configuration.

2. Explain carefully why two lines which intersect in only one point may be inverted into curves which intersect in two distinct points.

3. If two circles are orthogonal, prove that the inverse of the center of one, with respect to the other, is the midpoint of their common chord.

4. Construct a circle tangent to a given circle, at a given point on the circle, and orthogonal to a second given circle.

5. If a given circle is to be inverted into itself, what is the locus for all possible centers of inversion?

6. Construct a circle cutting three given lines in three given angles. *Hint:* start with an arbitrary circle and construct lines, parallel to the given ones, meeting this circle in the specified angles; then use a homothetic transformation.

7. Let $ABCDE$ be a convex pentagon inscribed in a circle. Use the method employed in Ptolemy's Theorem to derive a relationship connecting certain line segments. Let two vertices, say D and E, coincide and see if the relation reduces to Ptolemy's Theorem.

8. Decorative designs may be obtained by inverting simple designs. A table top is composed of 9 squares with each corner square and the center square black and with the remaining 4 squares white. Invert this design with respect to a circle inscribed in the center square to prepare a design for a round table top.

★9. Let the circle with center at the point (0,0) and radius 1 be a circle of inversion. Find the co-ordinates of the image of a general point in both rectangular and polar co-ordinates.

★10. Using the result of Exercise 9, find the equation of the curve inverse to $a(x^2 + y^2) + bx + cy + d = 0$. Let the circle of inversion be a unit circle with center at the origin. Use this equation to prove Theorems 1, 2, and 3 of § 6.2.

★11. Use the result of Exercise 9 to find the polar co-ordinate equation of one or more conic sections. Choose a focus for each center of inversion.

★12. Sketch the inverse curve of a parabola with the focus as the center of inversion. Exercises 9 or 11 may be used.

7

Projective Properties

~~~~~~

7.1 THE DOUBLE-RATIO

Definition 1. *Let π and π' be any two given planes and let O be a given point on neither π nor π'. A **central projection** of π onto π', with O as the **center of projection,** is obtained by letting the image of each point P on plane π be the point P' in which the line OP cuts plane π'.*

If the center of projection is an ideal point, the transformation of Definition 1 is called a *parallel projection.* A *projective transformation* is a succession (or product) of one or more central or parallel projections. The image of a figure, in a projective transformation, is the figure formed by the images of all points of the original figure.

A study of projective geometry should stress properties which remain invariant in a projective transformation. For example, the projective image of a triangle is a second triangle, not necessarily similar to the first. From the analytic geometry definition of a conic as a section of a cone, the student should realize that a circle may be projected into an ellipse, parabola, or hyperbola. It follows that the projective image of any conic is another conic.

A geometric figure in a plane may be projected into another figure in the same plane by a succession of two central projections, the first onto a second plane, the second back onto the original plane. Since this general transformation involves three-dimensional geometry, it cannot be carried out in one plane using straightedge and compass. There are, however, special cases which are useful in geometric constructions; using a special case of Definition 1, points on one line may be projected into points on a second line in the same plane.

Definition 2. *Let l and l' be two lines in the same plane π and let O be a given point in the plane π but on neither l nor l'. A **central projection** of l onto l', with O as the center of projection, is obtained by letting the image of each point P on line l be the point P' in which the line OP cuts line l'.*

As in Definition 1, the transformation in Definition 2 is called a parallel projection if O is an ideal point.

Problem 1. *Given points A, B, and C on line l, and points A', B', and C' on line l', find a succession of central projections carrying A, B, and C into A', B', and C' respectively.*

Solution: The given elements are shown in Figure 66. Let O be a convenient point on AA' and from center O project A, B, and C into corresponding points A'', B'', and C'' on line $A'B$, so that A'' is A' and

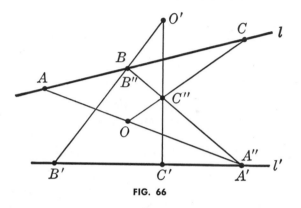

FIG. 66

B'' is B. Let $B'B''$ and $C'C''$ intersect at O'. From center O' points A'', B'', and C'' project into A', B', and C' respectively on line l'.

In Figure 66, AC/CB is not equal to $A'C'/C'B'$, so the ratio in which a point divides a line segment is not invariant under projection. However, when four collinear points are projected, the ratio discussed below does remain unchanged.

Definition 3. *If points A, B, C, and D are collinear, the ratio* $\dfrac{AC}{CB} \div \dfrac{AD}{DB}$, *represented by the symbol $(ABCD)$, is called the **double-ratio** of the points.*

The line segments in Definition 3 are directed segments. If one of the points is an ideal point, the definition is modified as suggested by a limit process; for example, if D is an ideal point, $AD/DB = -1$, by definition, so that $(ABC\infty) = -AC/CB$.

Theorem 1. *The double-ratio of four points is invariant under projection.*

Proof: For a parallel projection the student should prove the theorem using elementary properties of similar triangles.

For a central projection, see Figure 67, let a, b, c, and d be lines joining the collinear points A, B, C, and D respectively to point P. Let an arbitrary line cut a, b, c, and d in points A', B', C', and D'. It is to be proved that $(ABCD) = (A'B'C'D')$.

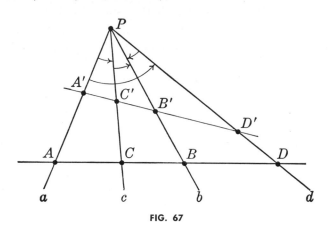

FIG. 67

At present, directed segments are neglected and all segments are considered positive. From the definition of $(ABCD)$ and the use of the Law of Sines, it follows that

$$(ABCD) = \frac{AC}{CB} \div \frac{AD}{DB} = \frac{\dfrac{AC}{PC}}{\dfrac{CB}{PC}} \div \frac{\dfrac{AD}{PD}}{\dfrac{DB}{PD}} = \frac{\dfrac{\sin \angle APC}{\sin \angle PAC}}{\dfrac{\sin \angle CPB}{\sin \angle CBP}} \div \frac{\dfrac{\sin \angle APD}{\sin \angle PAD}}{\dfrac{\sin \angle DPB}{\sin \angle PBD}}.$$

Note that angles PAC and PAD are either equal or supplementary, depending on the location of points A, C, and D. In both of these cases $\sin \angle PAC = \sin \angle PAD$. Likewise, $\sin \angle CBP = \sin \angle PBD$. These substitutions lead to the simplified result

$$(ABCD) = \frac{\sin \angle APC}{\sin \angle CPB} \div \frac{\sin \angle APD}{\sin \angle DPB}.$$

The above discussion is not valid if one of the points A, B, C, or D is an ideal point. Let D be an ideal point so that, by Definition 3,

$$(ABCD) = -\frac{AC}{CB}.$$

Then, as above, with direction neglected,

$$(ABCD) = \frac{\dfrac{\sin \angle APC}{\sin \angle PAC}}{\dfrac{\sin \angle CPB}{\sin \angle CBP}}.$$

In this case angles PAC and APD are supplementary (or equal), since AB is parallel to d, so that $\sin \angle PAC = \sin \angle APD$. In the same way $\sin \angle CBP = \sin \angle DPB$. For the special case under discussion

$$(ABCD) = \frac{\sin \searrow APC}{\sin \angle CPB} \div \frac{\sin \angle APD}{\sin \angle DPB}.$$

This result shows that the numerical value of $(ABCD)$ depends only on the angles formed by lines a, b, c, and d at the point P. Since A', B', C', and D' are also on a, b, c, and d, respectively. It follows that the absolute values of the double-ratios $(ABCD)$ and $(A'B'C'D')$ are equal.

The double-ratio $(ABCD)$ is negative if and only if one of the points C or D divides the segment AB internally and the other point divides the segment AB externally. Let the angles in the above expression for $(ABCD)$ be positive for counterclockwise rotation and negative for clockwise rotation. The equality then has the correct sign, in addition to the correct numerical value, since an odd number of the four angles are negative if and only if $(ABCD)$ is negative. This completes the proof that $(ABCD) = (A'B'C'D')$.

EXERCISES

1. In a central projection of plane π onto plane π', what points are fixed?

2. Is the double-ratio of four points invariant in every rigid motion transformation?

3. Prove that the double-ratio of four points is invariant in a parallel projection.

4. Let A and B be ordinary points and let I be the ideal point on the line through A and B. Choose a line q and a point Q so that in a central projection on q with center Q: A' is an ideal point, B and B' coincide, and I' is an ordinary point.

5. Describe a central projection of one plane onto a second in which two given parallel lines in the first plane have as images, in the second plane, two intersecting lines.

6. Given a quadrilateral, describe a central projection which carries the quadrilateral into some parallelogram.

7. Use Theorem 1 to show that a projective transformation which carries three points of a line into the same three points, carries every point of the line into itself.

7.2 HARMONIC ELEMENTS

The order in which collinear points are taken is an essential part of the definition of the double-ratio of the points. For example, if

$(ABCD) = r$, $(BACD) = 1/r$. The reader may wish to verify that for the 24 permutations of the letters in the symbol for the double-ratio, only six different values are possible. If $(ABCD) = -1$, the points C and D divide the segment AB internally and externally in the same ratio; this case is important enough to deserve a special definition.

Definition 1. *The collinear points A, B, C, D form a* **harmonic range** *if $(ABCD) = -1$. In this case, C and D are called* **harmonic conjugates** *with respect to A and B, and D is called the* **fourth harmonic** *of C with respect to A and B.*

Problem 1. *Given three collinear points, construct a fourth harmonic.*

Discussion: Several solutions are possible, since the fourth point can be the fourth harmonic of any of the three given points with respect to the other two. If the given points are X, Y, Z and if the point W is to be the fourth harmonic of Y with respect to Z and X, then $(ZXYW) = -1$. This requires that $\dfrac{ZY}{YX} = -\dfrac{ZW}{WX}$. Since the given points determine the ratio $\dfrac{ZY}{YX}$, the point W can be found by the method of Problem 1, § 2.1.

This problem is equivalent to Problem 1, § 2.7, whose solution does not require a compass.

Theorem 1. *A point P and its inverse point P' are harmonic conjugates with respect to the points in which the line PP' cuts the circle of inversion.*

Proof: Let P and P', Figure 68, be inverse points with respect to the circle with center O and radius r, so that $OP \cdot OP' = r^2$. Let the line PP' cut the circle of inversion in points A and B. To show that $(ABPP') = -1$, it is sufficient to show that $AP \cdot P'B = -PB \cdot AP'$.

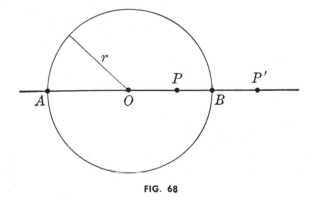

FIG. 68

Using directed segments, we find that

$$AP \cdot P'B = (AO + OP)(P'O + OB) = (r + OP)(r - OP')$$
$$= r^2 + r(OP - OP') - OP \cdot OP' = r(OP - OP').$$

Likewise,

$$PB \cdot AP' = (PO + OB)(AO + OP') = (r - OP)(r + OP')$$
$$= r^2 + r(OP' - OP) - OP \cdot OP' = -r(OP - OP').$$

Hence $(ABCD) = -1$.

Theorem 1 shows that the idea of a harmonic range is closely associated with inversion. For example, if P and P' are harmonic conjugates with respect to A and B, then P and P' are inverse points with respect to the circle with AB as diameter. This means that any construction for inverse points may be utilized in constructing a fourth harmonic, and conversely.

The expression **pencil of lines** may be used to designate several lines (or, in some cases, the entire family of lines) passing through a fixed point.

Theorem 2. *If a pencil of four lines divides one transversal harmonically, it divides every transversal harmonically.*

Proof: This is a special case of Theorem 1 of § 7.1; it is equivalent to the statement that a harmonic range is invariant in a projection.

Definition 2. *Let the lines a, b, c, and d join the point P to the collinear points A, B, C, and D respectively. If $(ABCD) = -1$, the lines are said to form a* **harmonic pencil,** *with vertex P, and this relation is designated by $(abcd) = -1$. Lines c and d are* **harmonic conjugates** *with respect to a and b; d is the* **fourth harmonic** *of c with respect to a and b.*

To show that four concurrent lines form a harmonic pencil, it is sufficient to find one transversal which cuts the lines in points of a harmonic range. The problem of constructing a fourth harmonic to three concurrent lines is easily solved by use of Problem 1.

Example 1. *If two conjugate lines in a harmonic pencil are perpendicular, prove that they bisect the angles between the other lines of the harmonic pencil.*

Solution: In Figure 69, let $(abcd) = -1$ and let c and d be perpendicular. Let any transversal parallel to d cut the pencil in the ordinary points A, B, and C and in the ideal point D. By Definition 2, the harmonic pencil cuts at least one transversal harmonically and hence, by Theorem 2, it must cut every transversal harmonically. Thus we have $(ABCD) = -1$. Since D is an ideal point, $-AC/CB = -1$ and $AC = CB$.

Triangles APC and BPC are congruent because $AC = CB$, $PC = PC$, and $\angle ACP = \angle BCP = 90°$, since both of lines d and AB are perpendicular to c. Thus angles APC and BPC are equal in magnitude and c must bisect one of the angles between lines a and b; it easily follows that d bisects the other angle between lines a and b.

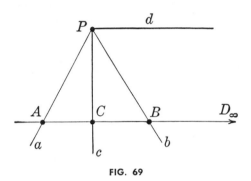

FIG. 69

EXERCISES

1. If A and B divide one diameter of a circle harmonically, and if C and D divide another diameter of the same circle harmonically, prove that A, B, C, and D are concyclic.

2. Four points on a given line form a harmonic range. After inversion, with respect to a center of inversion on the line, do the inverse points form a harmonic range?

3. If $(ABCD) = -1$ show that $1/AC + 1/AD = 2/AB$.

4. If three lines of a harmonic pencil intercept equal segments on a transversal, show that the transversal is parallel to the fourth line of the pencil.

5. In triangle ABC let A', B', and C' be the midpoints of sides BC, CA, and AB. Prove that lines $C'B$, $C'A'$, $C'C$, and $C'B'$ form a harmonic pencil.

6. Let A, B, C, D, P, and Q be concyclic points. If PA, PB, PC, and PD are harmonic lines, prove that QA, QB, QC, and QD also form a harmonic pencil.

7. Let A, B, C, and D form a harmonic range and let Q be any fifth point on the line AD. After inversion, with the center of inversion not on AD, prove that $Q'A'$, $Q'B'$, $Q'C'$, and $Q'D'$ form a harmonic pencil.

7.3   COMPLETE QUADRILATERAL

In elementary geometry, the word *quadrilateral* is usually associated with a four-sided polygon in which each interior angle is less than a straight angle; a more general definition is now given.

Definition 1. *A **complete quadrilateral** is composed of four lines, called sides, no three concurrent, and the six points, called vertices, which these sides determine. Two vertices not on a common side are called opposite. The three lines determined by pairs of opposite vertices are diagonal lines, and the three intersections of diagonal lines are diagonal points.*

The complete quadrilateral is closely associated with the harmonic ratio; in fact, the relation in the following theorem is sometimes used to define a harmonic range.

Theorem 1. *The vertices on any diagonal line of a complete quadrilateral are harmonic conjugates with respect to the diagonal points on the same diagonal.*

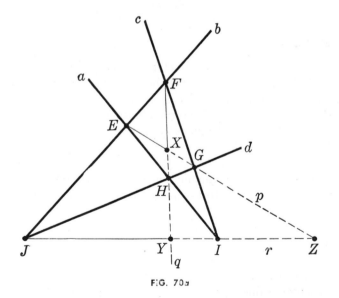

FIG. 70a

Proof: In Figure 70a, the complete quadrilateral is determined by sides a, b, c, and d. These sides determine the vertices E, F, G, H, I, J and the diagonal points X, Y, Z. It is to be proved that $(JIYZ) = -1$, $(FHXY) = -1$, and $(EGXZ) = -1$.

The solution of Problem 1 of § 2.7 (with the notation of Figure 24 changed to agree with that of Figure 70a) uses the Theorems of Ceva and Menelaus to prove that $(JIYZ) = -1$. A central projection from point F onto line EZ carries the points J, I, Y, Z into the points E, G, X, Z. These last points are projected into points F, H, X, Y on line FY when J is used as the center of projection. Hence, by Theorem 2 of § 7.2,

$$(JIYZ) = (EGXZ) = (FHXY) = -1.$$

Theorem 1 provides a method for constructing the fourth harmonic to three given collinear points without use of a compass. This is the same construction as considered in Problem 1 of § 2.7.

If, instead of starting with four lines to determine a complete quadrilateral, four given points are taken as vertices, a configuration called a complete quadrangle may be defined.

Definition 2. *A **complete quadrangle** is composed of four points, called vertices, no three collinear, and the six lines, called sides, which these vertices determine. Two sides not through the same vertex are called opposite. The three points determined by pairs of opposite sides are diagonal points, and the three lines connecting diagonal points are diagonal lines.*

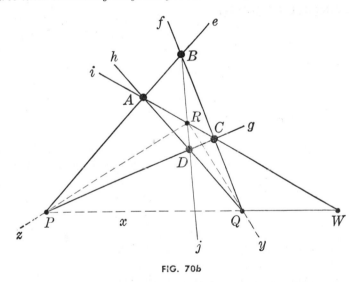

FIG. 70b

In Figure 70b, the complete quadrangle is determined by vertices $A, B, C,$ and D. These vertices determine the sides e, f, g, h, i, j and the diagonal lines x, y, z. In Figure 70a and 70b the simple quadrilateral determined by sides $a, b, c,$ and d is the same as the simple quadrilateral determined by the consecutive vertices A, B, C, and D. Note, however, that the diagonal lines of Figure 70a and the diagonal points of Figure 70b do not determine the same triangle.

EXERCISES

1. In Figure 70a, prove that $(EGXZ) = -1$ by direct use of the theorems of Ceva and Menelaus.

2. Given three concurrent lines, construct a fourth harmonic without use of a compass.

3. Given a line segment AB and a line parallel to AB, locate the midpoint of AB using a straightedge only.

4. Let D be the foot of the altitude from vertex A in triangle ABC. Let P be any point on AD. Let BP cut AC at R, and let CP cut AB at S. Prove that angles SDA and RDA are equal. (This exercise will be solved in § 7.6).

5. Provide definitions for a complete trilateral and for a complete triangle. Do these configurations differ from an ordinary triangle?

7.4 PRINCIPLE OF DUALITY

The most noticeable difference between the postulates of Euclidean plane geometry and those used in projective geometry is concerned with the Euclidean postulate that through a given point, one and only one line can be drawn parallel to a given line. Since parallel lines, in the Euclidean sense, do not project into parallel lines, the word *parallel* is unnecessary in projective geometry. Indeed, a fundamental postulate of projective geometry states that two distinct lines in the same plane intersect in exactly one point. If parallel lines are defined as lines in the same plane which do not meet, then in projective geometry there is no line through a given point parallel to a given line.

There is a popular misconception that the postulates of Euclidean geometry are really true statements about space relations and that any different postulate system is not actually satisfied by physical objects. It has been shown that the parallel postulate is independent of the other postulates of Euclidean geometry so that the parallel postulate cannot be "proved" true. The "truth" of the parallel postulate cannot be verified by experimental methods since it involves behavior at a distance too remote for observation. Two systems of geometry, with different postulates concerning parallel lines, may be equally plausible; each may have practical applications; a great many common theorems may be true in both systems.

A property of a figure such as the length of a line segment or the magnitude of an angle, that depends upon measurement is called a **metric** property. Many postulates of Euclidean geometry deal with metric properties and since such postulates are not needed in a study restricted to projective properties only, fewer postulates are required in projective geometry than in Euclidean geometry.

Many of the postulates of projective geometry deal with incidence relations between the undefined terms *point* and *line*. These postulates have the interesting and useful property that if the words *point* and *line* are interchanged in the statement of any postulate, the resulting statement is also a postulate in the system.

When we say that the words *line* and *point* are interchanged in a geometrical statement we shall imply that other necessary modifications are made in the English structure of the statement. For example, the phrase "two lines *through* a point" will be changed to "two points *on* a line." The word *collinear* will be replaced by *concurrent*, since the former means "on a line" and the latter means "through a point." Likewise, *quadrilateral* will be replaced by *quadrangle*.

If in a postulate, definition, or theorem concerning points and lines in a plane, the word *point* is replaced by *line* and the word *line* is replaced by *point* each time one of these words appears (or is implied), the resulting statement is called the **dual** of the original postulate, definition, or theorem.

Let the dual of each postulate also be a postulate in a geometrical system. Let the dual of each definition also be another definition. The **principle of duality** states that the dual of each true theorem will also be a true theorem in this system. This principle is based on the observation that, since the proof of a theorem uses certain postulates, and perhaps some definitions, the proof of a dual theorem can be made by replacing each postulate and definition by the corresponding dual.

Since a rigorous development of projective geometry, starting with postulates, has not been presented in this book, it is not possible to say that a theorem which has been proved has a dual which can be accepted as true without further verification. The principle of duality can, however, suggest that a related theorem may be true and thus motivate an attempted proof. The following examples illustrate dual statements.

POSTULATES	DUAL POSTULATES
1. Through every point pass an unlimited number of lines.	1. On every line there are an unlimited number of points.
2. Two distinct points determine one line.	2. Two distinct lines determine one point.

3. A triangle is a figure composed of three points, not collinear, and the three lines determined by these points.

4. Complete quadrilateral, Definition 1, § 7.3.

5. The points A, B, C, and D on line p and the points A', B', C', and D' on line p' are *perspective* if and only if lines AA', BB', CC', and DD' are concurrent.

3. A trilateral is a figure composed of three lines, not concurrent, and the three points determined by these lines.

4. Complete quadrangle, Definition 2, § 7.3.

5. The lines a, b, c, and d through point P and the lines a', b', c', and d' through point P' are *perspective* if and only if the points of intersection of a and a', of b and b', of c and c', and of d and d' are collinear.

6. If points A, B, C, and D on line p and points A', B', C', and D' on line p' are perspective and if $(ABCD) = -1$, then $(A'B'C'D') = -1$.

7. Theorem 1, § 7.3.

6. If lines a, b, c, and d through P and lines a', b', c', and d' through P' are perspective and if $(abcd) = -1$, then $(a'b'c'd') = -1$.

7. Theorem 1, below.

8. Given the collinear points A, B, and C, find point D so that $(ABCD) = -1$.

9. Problem 2, § 5.1.

8. Given the concurrent lines a, b, and c, find line d so that $(abcd) = -1$.

9. Problem 1, below.

Theorem 1. *The sides through any diagonal point of a complete quadrangle are harmonic conjugates with respect to the diagonal lines through the same diagonal point.*

Proof: In Figure 70b, let P be an arbitrary one of the three diagonal points of the quadrangle determined by vertices A, B, C, and D. It is sufficient to prove that lines PA, PD, PR, and PQ form a harmonic pencil, or that $(egzx) = -1$. Let AC and PQ intersect at W. Then using the complete quadrilateral determined by lines e, f, g, and h, it follows, from Theorem 1 of § 7.3, that $(ACRW) = -1$. Hence, by Definition 2, § 7.2, $(egzx) = -1$.

Problem 1. *Let points A and B and line p be given. An obstruction between A and B prevents drawing line AB, directly, using a straightedge. Find the point in which line AB intersects line p.*

Discussion: If a student recalls that Problem 2, § 5.1, can be solved using any of the transformations discussed in Chapters 5 or 6, he may be able to devise several different solution methods for the present problem. One elementary solution is described here.

In Figure 71, let the shaded area be an obstruction through which no line can be drawn. Pick a convenient point, P, on line p so that lines PA and PB can be drawn and so that the line CD, through the midpoints of PA and PB respectively, does not pass through the obstruction. (If

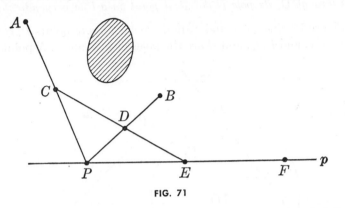

FIG. 71

such a point P does not exist, a modification must be made.) Let CD cut line p at E. Locate F on p so that $PE = EF$. That F is the intersection of AB and p follows from elementary properties of similar triangles.

EXERCISES

1. State the duals of Definition 1 and Theorem 1 of § 7.1.

2. Are the Theorems of Ceva and Menelaus dual theorems?

3. Explain a method for using inversion to solve Problem 1 of this section.

4. How many lines are determined by n points in a plane if no three points are collinear? What is the dual of this result?

5. A harmonic pencil and a harmonic range are dual configurations. Show, however, that Definitions 1 and 2 in § 7.2 are not dual definitions. Provide an alternate definition for a harmonic range using the property of Theorem 1, § 7.3, and dualize this definition to define a harmonic pencil.

6. State the dual of Problem 1, § 7.1. Solve this new problem by the process of dualizing each step in the solution given in § 7.1.

7.5 POLE AND POLAR

The transformation discussed in this section provides a unique correspondence between the points in the plane and the lines in a plane and changes a figure composed of points and lines into a dual figure.

Definition 1. *Let a given circle have center at O, let P and P' be inverse points with respect to this circle, and let p be the line perpendicular to OP' at P'. Then p is called the* **polar line** *of P, and P is called the* **pole** *of p with respect to the given circle. The polar line of O is the ideal line; if p passes through O, its pole is the ideal point on a line perpendicular to p.*

In Figure 72, lines p, q, and r are the polar lines of points P, Q, and R respectively, and P, Q, and R are the poles of p, q, and r. A point lies on

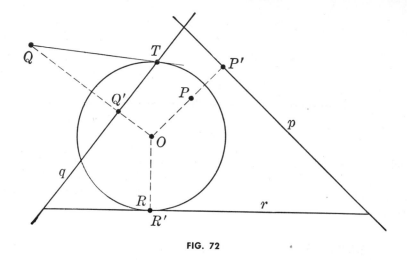

FIG. 72

its polar line with respect to a circle if and only if it is on the circumference of the circle. In Figure 72, let q cut circle O at T. A previous method for constructing inverse points (the second solution of Problem 1, § 6.1) shows that QT is tangent to circle O. The fact that the polar line of an external point cuts the polar circle in points of contact of tangent lines from the external point will be used in later constructions.

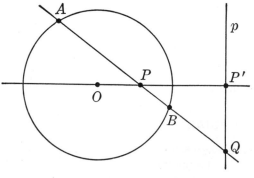

FIG. 73

Theorem 1. *If p is the polar of P with respect to a circle, any line through P, cutting the circle, is divided harmonically by P, p, and the circle.*

Proof: Let P' be the intersection of OP and p, Figure 73. Let any line through P cut the circle at A and B and cut p at Q. Since angle $PP'Q$ is a right angle, the circle with PQ as diameter passes through P' and by Theorem 3, § 6.5, this circle is orthogonal to circle O, and A and B are inverse points with respect to the circle with PQ as diameter. From Theorem 1, § 7.2, it follows that $(ABPQ) = -1$.

Theorem 2. *If P is a point on the line q, the polar line of P passes through the pole of q.*

Proof: Let P be a point on q, Figure 74, and let p and Q be the corresponding polar and pole with respect to circle O. It is to be proved that Q lies on p. Let P' on p and Q' on q be the inverse points of P and Q respectively. The circle through P', P, and Q' is orthogonal to circle O

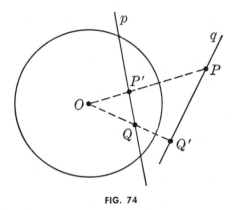

FIG. 74

and must pass through Q by Theorem 3, § 6.5. Since the quadrilateral $P'PQ'Q$ is cyclic and angle $PQ'Q$ is a right angle, the angle $PP'Q$ is also a right angle. Since line p is perpendicular to PP' at P', point Q must lie on p.

As an exercise, the student should point out why the above proof is not valid if either of P or Q is on circle O or if q passes through point O. If either P or Q lies on circle O, the proof may be based on the method (Problem 1, § 6.1) for constructing inverse points. If q passes through O, line p must be perpendicular to line q. Hence, by Definition 1, Q is the ideal point on p.

Theorem 3. *If four points form a harmonic range, their polars form a harmonic pencil.*

Analysis. If A, B, C, and D are harmonic points on a line p, the polars are lines a, b, c, and d through point P, the pole of p, by Theorem 2. Let O be the center of the polar circle. Since lines a, b, c, and d are perpendicular to OA, OB, OC, and OD, the angle between two lines of the pencil through O is equal to the angle between the corresponding lines of the pencil through P. Since the pencil with vertex at O is harmonic, the pencil through P is also harmonic by Definition 1, § 7.2, and by the proof of Theorem 1, § 7.1.

EXERCISES

1. Construct the image of a given triangle in a polar transformation.
2. If M is the midpoint of segment AB, and if I is the ideal point on the line through AB, construct the polar lines of A, B, M, and I, with respect to a given circle.
3. In a polar transformation determined by a given circle, two points are called **conjugate points** if each lies on the polar line of the other. Given a point on a given line, find the conjugate point on the line, in a polar transformation.
4. If two conjugate points with respect to a circle (see Exercise 3) lie on a secant of the circle, show that these points and the points of intersection of the circle and the secant form a harmonic range.
5. Describe the configuration obtained by subjecting a complete quadrilateral to a polar transformation.
6. Describe the family of lines composed of the polar lines of all points on a fixed circle.

7.6 MISCELLANEOUS THEOREMS

In some cases, introduction of harmonic properties may simplify the proof of a Euclidean geometry theorem concerned with metric properties. Theorems 1 and 2 are examples of theorems which involve only elementary concepts but whose proofs are difficult for a student with no knowledge of properties of harmonic elements. Theorem 1 is sometimes called the **butterfly problem** because of the resemblance suggested in Figure 75.

Theorem 1. *Let M be the midpoint of a fixed chord PQ in a given circle. Draw two arbitrary chords through M and connect the end-points of these chords to form two other chords cutting PQ in points R and S. Then, $RM = MS$.*

Proof: In Figure 75, AB and CD are arbitrary chords through M, the midpoint of chord PQ in a given circle. Chords AD and CB cut PQ

in points R and S. As in Theorem 1, § 7.1,

$$(PRMQ) = \frac{\sin \angle PAB}{\sin \angle BAD} \div \frac{\sin \angle PAQ}{\sin \angle QAD}$$

and

$$(PMSQ) = \frac{\sin \angle PCB}{\sin \angle BCD} \div \frac{\sin \angle PCQ}{\sin \angle QCD}.$$

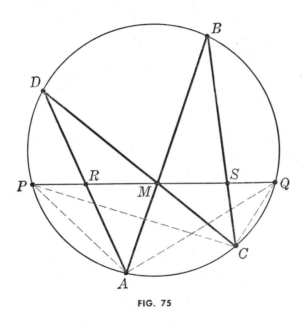

FIG. 75

Since angles inscribed in the same arc are equal, it follows that $(PRMQ) = (PMSQ)$ and, therefore,

$$\frac{PM}{MR} \cdot \frac{QR}{PQ} = \frac{PS}{SM} \cdot \frac{QM}{PQ}.$$

This is equivalent to

$$PM \cdot QR \cdot SM = PS \cdot QM \cdot MR$$

and since $PM = MQ$

$$QR \cdot SM = -PS \cdot MR, \quad \text{or} \quad RQ \cdot MS = PS \cdot RM.$$

Let $RQ = RM + MQ$ and $PS = PM + MS$ to obtain

$$RM \cdot MS + MQ \cdot MS - PM \cdot RM + MS \cdot RM.$$

This reduces to $MQ \cdot MS = PM \cdot RM$ and, since $MQ = PM$, it follows that $MS = RM$.

Theorem 2. *Let P be a point on one altitude of triangle ABC. Let PA, PB, and PC cut sides of the triangle in points L, M, and N. Then, the altitude through P bisects an angle of triangle LMN.*

Proof: Assume that P is on the altitude through A, Figure 76. It is then to be shown that LA bisects angle MLN. In some cases, Figure 76b, LA bisects the exterior angle of triangle MLN.

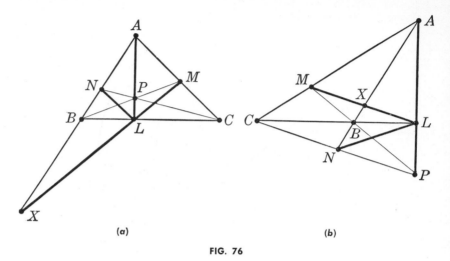

(a)   (b)

FIG. 76

Let AB and LM intersect at X. In the complete quadrilateral with vertices at points A, B, P, L, M, and C, lines MX and CN are diagonal lines and, by Theorem 1 of § 7.3, $(XNBA) = -1$. Hence the pencil of lines, with vertex at L, passing through points X, N, B, and A is harmonic with LM and LN harmonic conjugates of the perpendicular lines LA and LB. By Example 1, § 7.2, LA and LB bisect the angles between lines LM and LN.

Theorem 3. *If the vertices of a complete quadrangle lie on a circle, each diagonal point is the pole, with respect to the circle, of the line through the other diagonal points.*

Proof: In Figure 77, let A, B, C, and D be concyclic vertices of a complete quadrangle. Let K be an arbitrary one of the three diagonal points and let the other diagonal points be E and F.

Since points A, B, C, D, E, and F are vertices of a complete quadrilateral, with diagonal points K, L, and M, Theorem 1 of § 7.3 shows that $(CAKM) = -1$ and $(DBKL) = -1$.

From Theorem 1, § 7.5, if line CK cuts the polar line of K in point M', then $(CAKM') = -1$. The points M and M' must coincide, and it follows that M, and also L, must lie on the polar line of K. Since M and L are on line EF, EF is the polar line of K.

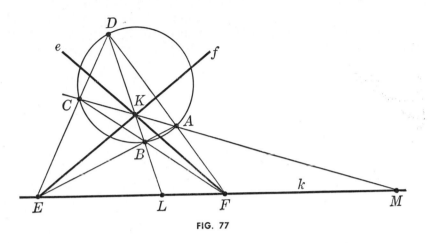

FIG. 77

Definition 1. *A triangle is called **self-polar** with respect to a circle if each vertex is the pole of the opposite side, and conversely.*

Theorem 3 states that the diagonal triangle of a concyclic quadrangle is self-polar.

EXERCISES

1. The triangle whose vertices are the feet of the altitudes in a given triangle is called the **orthic** or **pedal** triangle. Show that each altitude of a given triangle bisects an angle of the corresponding orthic triangle.

2. Given one vertex, construct a triangle self-polar with respect to a given circle. How many solutions are possible?

3. Show that a self-polar triangle is obtuse.

4. Show that the orthocenter of a self-polar triangle is the center of the polar circle.

5. Construct a circle so that a given obtuse triangle is self-polar with respect to the circle.

7.7 DESARGUES' THEOREM

The Theorem discussed in this section is named for Gerard Desargues (1593-1662). Desargues is credited with introducing ideal points and ideal lines into geometry. This theorem, which is of fundamental importance in projective geometry, does not involve any metric properties.

Theorem 1. *If lines joining corresponding vertices of two triangles are concurrent, the intersections of corresponding sides are collinear.*

Proof: In Figure 78, lines AA', BB', and CC' meet at O. Let AB and $A'B'$ intersect at X, BC and $B'C'$ intersect at Y, and CA and $C'A'$ intersect at Z. We wish to show that the points X, Y, Z are collinear.

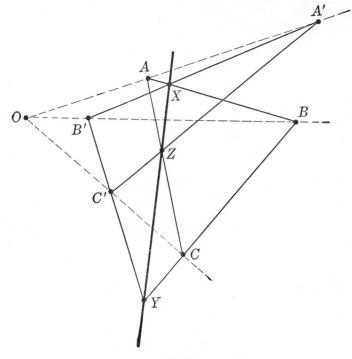

FIG. 78

Consider $A'B'$ as a transversal of triangle OAB, cutting OA in A', AB in X, and BO in B'. By the Theorem of Menelaus, § 2.5,

$$\frac{OA'}{A'A} \cdot \frac{AX}{XB} \cdot \frac{BB'}{B'O} = -1.$$

Consider $B'C'$ as a transversal of triangle OBC to obtain

$$\frac{OB'}{B'B} \cdot \frac{BY}{YC} \cdot \frac{CC'}{C'O} = -1.$$

Likewise, with $C'A'$ as a transversal of triangle OCA,

$$\frac{OC'}{C'C} \cdot \frac{CZ}{ZA} \cdot \frac{AA'}{A'O} = -1.$$

The product of the last three equalities, with cancellations, taking directions of segments into account, gives

$$\frac{AX}{XB} \cdot \frac{BY}{YC} \cdot \frac{CZ}{ZA} = -1.$$

The Theorem of Menelaus, applied to triangle ABC, shows that points X, Y, and Z are collinear.

In previous work with transformations a problem, concerning properties invariant in the transformation under discussion, was usually solved by first making a transformation changing the problem to a more convenient form. Since concurrent lines and collinear points remain concurrent lines and collinear points, under a central projection, Theorem 1 is true if and only if it remains true in any central projection onto another plane. It is possible to project any two points, say X and Y, into ideal points by projecting from a point P onto a plane parallel to the plane determined by points P, X, and Y.

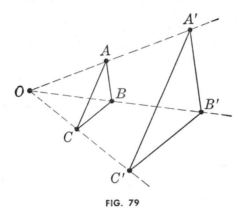

FIG. 79

Suppose that the configuration of Figure 78 is projected into the configuration of Figure 79 where X and Y are ideal points so that AB and $A'B'$ are parallel and that BC and $B'C'$ are also parallel. To prove Theorem 1, it is only necessary to show that Z is an ideal point, or that AC and $A'C'$ are parallel.

By elementary properties of similar triangles it follows that

$$\frac{OA}{OA'} = \frac{OB}{OB'} \quad \text{and} \quad \frac{OB}{OB'} = \frac{OC}{OC'}.$$

It is, therefore, apparent that $\dfrac{OA}{OA'} = \dfrac{OC}{OC'}$ and that AC and $A'C'$ are parallel.

To prove the converse of Theorem 1 assume that, in Figure 78, points X, Y, and Z are collinear. It is to be proved that AA', BB', and CC' are concurrent lines. These lines must be concurrent if their images are concurrent in any central projection onto another plane. Let us project the configuration of Figure 78 into a new configuration in which points X and Y become ideal points; this projection must also carry Z into an ideal point, since X, Y, and Z are collinear. The resulting configuration is illustrated in Figure 79 where corresponding sides of triangles ABC and $A'B'C'$ are parallel. Hence, by Theorem 3 of § 5.4, these triangles are homothetic; lines joining corresponding vertices must, therefore, be concurrent.

In the terminology of projective geometry, Desargues' Theorem and its converse may be stated as in Theorem 2.

Theorem 2. *Two triangles perspective from a point are perspective from a line and conversely.*

Desargues' Theorem is also true when triangles ABC and $A'B'C'$ lie in two different planes, and for this case the proof may be made using very simple properties of elementary solid geometry.

In Figure 78 assume the AA', BB', and CC' meet at O but that triangle ABC is in plane π and that triangle $A'B'C'$ is in a plane π', not parallel to π. Then lines AB and $A'B'$ are both in plane AOB and must meet in a point, say X. Likewise BC and $B'C'$ are in a plane and meet at Y, and CA and $C'A'$ meet at Z. Each of the three points X, Y, and Z are in plane π, since each is on a line in plane π. Likewise each of the points X, Y, and Z lies in plane π'. The points X, Y, and Z, therefore, lie on the line in which planes π and π' intersect.

EXERCISES

1. Let a line cut sides BC, CA, and AB of triangle ABC in points L, M, and N respectively. Let L', M', and N' be points on the sides of ABC so that $(BCLL') = -1$, $(CAMM') = -1$, and $(ABNN') = -1$. Project the entire configuration into another plane so that points L and M become ideal points. Show that L', M', and N' become midpoints of the sides of the new triangle.

2. Use the result of Exercise 1 to prove the Theorem of Menelaus, Theorem 1 of § 2.5.

7.8 STRAIGHTEDGE CONSTRUCTIONS

Problem 1. *Given three concurrent lines, construct a fourth harmonic without use of a compass.*

Analysis: Use Theorem 1, § 7.4, and construct a suitable complete quadrangle, or use Definition 2, § 7.2, to change the problem to Problem 1 of § 7.2.

Problem 2. *Construct the polar line of a given point, with respect to a given circle, without use of a compass.*

Construction: In Figure 80, P is a given point and O is the given circle. Draw two secants, through P, cutting circle O in points A, B, C, and D as shown. Then P is one diagonal point of the complete quadrangle with vertices A, B, C, and D. Construct the other diagonal points R and S. Then RS is the polar line of P, by Theorem 3 of § 7.6. This construction is valid unless P is on the circumference of circle O.

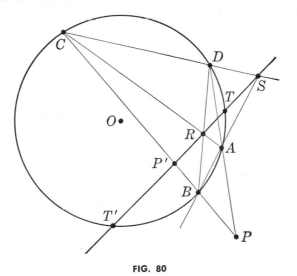

FIG. 80

If, in Figure 80, PB passes through O, the polar line of P cuts OP in P', the image of P in an inversion with respect to circle O. If P is outside O, the polar of P cuts the circle in points T and T' which are the points of contact of the tangents from P to circle O. These observations provide solutions for the next two problems.

Problem 3. *Construct the inverse of a given point with respect to a given circle, without use of a compass.*

Problem 4. *From an external point construct a tangent to a given circle, without use of a compass.*

Problem 5. *Construct a line through a given point and through the inaccessible intersection of two given lines, without use of a compass.*

Analysis: Apply the converse of Desargues' Theorem.

Construction: In Figure 81, let m and n be the given lines and let B be the given point. The notation of Figure 78 will be employed. Let A and A' be arbitrary points on m, and let C and C' be arbitrary points on n. Let AC and $A'C'$ intersect at Z. Through Z draw an arbitrary

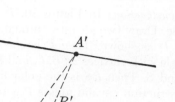

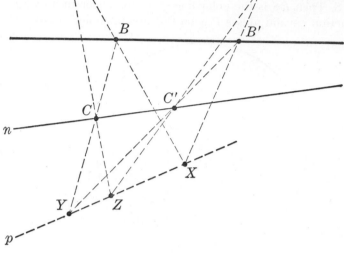

FIG. 81

line p. Let AB cut p at X, and let BC cut p at Y. Let $A'X$ and $C'Y$ intersect at B'. Then line BB' passes through the intersection of m and n.

EXERCISES

1. Construct the pole of a given line, with respect to a given circle, without use of a compass.

2. Solve Problem 1, § 7.4, without use of a compass.

3. Let M be the midpoint of a given segment AB. Through a given point P, construct a line parallel to AB, without use of a compass.

4. Construct a complete quadrilateral with a given triangle as the diagonal triangle. How many solutions are possible?

REVIEW EXERCISES

1. Given a point and a line, how many circles exist for which the point is the pole of the line? Describe the positions of all such circles.

2. If A, B, C, and D are fixed collinear points with $(ABCD) = r$, evaluate the double-ratio of these points for the 24 permutations of the letters A, B, C, and D in the double-ratio symbol.

3. Under what condition is the double-ratio of four points equal to $+1$?

4. Construct a triangle ABC, given vertices B and C, the point in which the bisector of angle A cuts BC, and the length of the median through A.

5. Let $(ABCD) = -1$ and $(A'B'C'D') = -1$. If AA', BB', and CC' are concurrent at P, must DD' also pass through P?

6. Given two lines m and n and a point P, use properties of harmonic elements to construct a line through P cutting the given lines in points M and N for which $MP = PN$.

7. A given straight line segment has an obstruction at one end. With straightedge only, extend the line segment beyond this obstruction.

8. Prove that the tangents to a circle at two vertices of an inscribed quadrangle meet in a point on a diagonal of the complete quadrangle.

9. If AB is a diameter of a given circle and CD is any chord perpendicular to AB, and if P is any point on the circumference of the circle, show that lines PA, PB, PC, and PD, taken in proper order, form a harmonic pencil.

10. Let A and B be fixed points. Let P and Q be variable points, on line AB, for which $(ABPQ) = -1$. As P moves continuously along the entire line AB, describe the resulting motion of point Q.

★11. Let a circle with its center, a line, and a point be given. Use a straightedge to construct a line through the given point parallel to the given line.

★12. Prove the converse of Desargues' Theorem for triangles in two non-parallel planes. Make a careful drawing.

★13. Prove that the polar line of the point (x',y'), with respect to the circle $x^2 + y^2 = r^2$, is $x'x + y'y = r^2$.

★14. Given the circle $x^2 + y^2 = 5$, find: (a) the polar line of the point $(3,-2)$; (b) the pole of the line $x - 2y = 3$; (c) the line tangent to the circle at the point $(2,-1)$.

★15. A table lamp has an opaque shade with an open circular top. Tell how to place the lamp in a corner of a room and tip the shade so that the shadows on two walls and the ceiling will be portions of an ellipse, a hyperbola, and a parabola.

8

Properties of Circles and Triangles

8.1 RADICAL AXIS

The present chapter contains assorted topics which have been selected to review previous material and to illustrate some of the numerous extensions of Euclidean geometry which are based on elementary work.

The first topic considered is related to a frequently used elementary theorem, Theorem 3 of § 2.4. If a line through a fixed point P cuts a fixed circle in points A and B, the product of PA and PB is a constant. Indeed, if the given circle has center O and radius r, Figure 82, it can be shown that the absolute value of $PA \cdot PB$ is $(OP)^2 - r^2$ for P outside the circle and $r^2 - (OP)^2$ for P inside the circle.

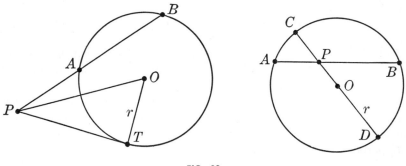

FIG. 82

Definition 1. *If P is any point in the same plane as a given circle with center O and radius r, the quantity $(OP)^2 - r^2$ is called the* **power** *of the point with respect to the circle.*

If P is outside circle O, the power is positive; if P is on the circumference, the power is zero; if P is inside circle O, the power is negative.

The student should verify that the locus of a point having a given power with respect to a given circle is a circle concentric with the given one. For a positive power, this is equivalent to Theorem 35 of § 1.10.

Definition 2. *The locus of a point, having equal powers with respect to two circles, is called the **radical axis** of the circles.*

Theorem 1. *The radical axis of two circles is a straight line perpendicular to the line of centers.*

Proof: Let the given circles have centers A and B and radii a and b, Figure 83. By Definitions 1 and 2, a point, P, is on the radical axis of circles A and B if and only if $(AP)^2 - a^2 = (BP)^2 - b^2$. Since this is equivalent to $(AP)^2 - (BP)^2 = a^2 - b^2$, Theorem 2, § 4.2, shows that the locus for P is a straight line perpendicular to AB.

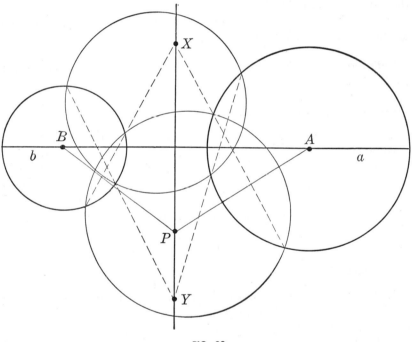

FIG. 83

If P is outside circle A, the power of P with respect to circle A is numerically equal to the square of the length of the tangent from P to circle A. This means that all points, from which equal tangents can be drawn to two circles, lie on the radical axis of the circles. It follows that the radical axis of two intersecting circles is the common chord of the circles.

Theorem 2. *The radical axes of three given circles are concurrent.*

The proof of this theorem is left as an exercise. If the circles have collinear centers, the parallel radical axes meet in an ideal point.

Definition 3. *The point of intersection of the radical axes of three circles is called the **radical center** of the circles.*

Problem 1. *Construct the radical axis of two given circles.*

Solution: If the circles intersect, draw their common chord; if they are tangent, construct their common tangent; otherwise, apply Theorem 2 as follows: Let the given circles be A and B, Figure 83, draw any convenient third circle intersecting circles A and B, and let the common chords of this circle and of circles A and B intersect at X. Since X is the radical center of all three circles, X must be one point on the radical axis of circles A and B. In the same manner, draw a fourth circle and locate Y, a second point on the desired radical axis.

Definition 4. *A circle orthogonal to three circles is called the **radical circle** of the given circles.*

Problem 2. *Construct the radical circle of three given circles.*

Solution: If the radical center is outside one circle, and therefore outside each circle, it is the center of the desired circle. The radius of the circle, orthogonal to each of the three given circles, is the squaᵣ.e root of the power of the radical center with respect to any one of the given circles.

There is no solution if the radical center is inside one of the given circles.

EXERCISES

1. A circle and a constant are given. Construct the locus of a point P so that the power of P with respect to the given circle is the given constant. Is the locus real for every value of the given constant?

2. If P is inside a circle with center O and radius r, and if a line through P cuts the circle at A and B, prove that the absolute value of the product of PA and PB is $r^2 - (OP)^2$.

3. Find a real circle of inversion for which three given circles remain unchanged. Discuss special cases. Can more than one solution exist?

4. If the center of a circle of inversion is a point on the radical circle of three given circles, show that these circles invert into circles with collinear centers.

5. In an inversion with respect to circle O, line l is the image of circle L. Prove that l is the radical axis of circles O and L.

8.2 COAXAL CIRCLES

Definition 1. *Three or more circles are* **coaxal** *if every pair of the circles has the same radical axis.*

The circles in the family of circles through two given points are coaxal, since the line through the given points is the common chord of any two of the circles. These circles are said to form a *coaxal* **system.** Are there also coaxal systems of non-intersecting circles?

Theorem 1. *The family of circles having centers on a given line, and orthogonal to a given circle with the given line as a diameter, is a coaxal system.*

Proof: In Figure 84, let B be any point on the circumference of a given circle O, and let line r be perpendicular to OB at O. It is to be

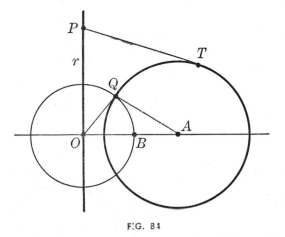

FIG. 84

shown that r is the radical axis of every pair of circles whose centers are on line OB and which are orthogonal to circle O.

Let A be the center of an arbitrary circle of this family and let circle A intersect circle O at Q. Let P be an arbitrary point on r and let T be a point of contact of a tangent from P to circle A.

The power of P with respect to circle A is $(PA)^2 - (AT)^2$. Using properties of right triangles,

$$(PA)^2 - (AT)^2 = (PO)^2 + (AO)^2 - (AQ)^2 = (PO)^2 + (OQ)^2$$
$$= (PO)^2 + (OB)^2 = (PB)^2.$$

Since the power of P with respect to circle A is independent of the location of circle A, if A is any circle of the family being considered, Definition 2, § 8.1, shows that line r is the radical axis for any two circles of the family.

It has been pointed out that the circles of a coaxal system may have two points in common or no points in common. The family of all circles tangent to a given line at a given point is also a coaxal system since the line is the radical axis for any two of the circles.

For circles in a coaxal system, the radical axis is considered to be a member of the coaxal system. Two given circles are sufficient to determine a coaxal system. If the given circles intersect, or are tangent, the problem of constructing a circle of the coaxal system, passing through a given point is trivial. If the circles do not intersect, Theorem 1 may be applied to find other circles of the coaxal system as in Problem 1, below.

The student should recall the method of analytic geometry for solving the equations of two circles simultaneously by first subtracting to obtain one linear equation which is the equation of the radical axis of the two circles. If the circles do not intersect in real points, the analytic solution yields imaginary points of intersection.

Usually no mention of imaginary points is included in a course in Euclidean geometry. If it is agreed, however, that three or more circles intersect in the same two points if and only if they belong to the same coaxal system, Problem 1 may be interpreted as a method for constructing a real circle through one given real point and two given imaginary points.

Problem 1. *Construct a circle passing through a given point and coaxal with two given non-intersecting circles.*

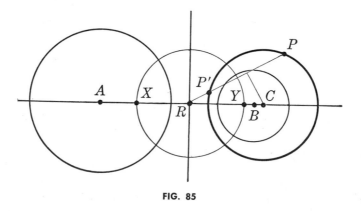

FIG. 85

Construction: Let circles A and B and point P be given, Figure 85. Construct the radical axis of these circles, cutting AB at R. Construct the circle, with center R, orthogonal to circles A and B. Construct P', the inverse of P with respect to circle R. Let the perpendicular bisector of PP' cut AB at C. The circle with center C and radius CP is orthogonal to circle R (Theorem 3 of § 6.5) and therefore coaxal with circles A and B (Theorem 1).

Let circle R cut AB in points X and Y as shown in Figure 85. These points are called *limiting points* of the coaxal system determined by circles A and B. From Theorem 3 of § 6.5, it follows that X and Y are inverse points with respect to any circle of the coaxal system. It also follows that any circle through X and Y will be orthogonal to every circle of the system determined by A and B. Therefore, the family of circles orthogonal to each member of a non-intersecting coaxal system is a coaxal system of intersecting circles

EXERCISES

1. Construct a circle coaxal with two given circles, passing through a given point.
2. Show that the inverse of the family of all lines parallel to a given line is a coaxal system of circles.
3. Use coaxal circles in describing the configuration obtained by inversion of: (*a*) the rectangular co-ordinate system; (*b*) the polar co-ordinate system.
4. A coaxal system of circles is inverted with respect to an arbitrary circle of inversion. Does the inverse configuration also form a coaxal system?

8.3   THE NINE-POINT CIRCLE

Much of the material in Euclidean geometry deals with special points, lines, and circles associated with a triangle. An imposing body of theorems concerning these topics has been developed during the past two centuries. An interesting example is the nine-point circle theorem; this theorem, showing that nine points associated with any triangle are cyclic, has been a favorite of geometry students since its discovery early in the nineteenth century.

The following notation is used. The vertices of a triangle are A, B, and C. The midpoints of the sides opposite A, B, and C are A', B', and C', in order. The feet of the altitudes through vertices A, B, and C are D, E, and F. The orthocenter is H; the centroid is G; the circumcenter is O; the midpoints of HA, HB, and HC are P, Q, and R respectively.

Theorem 1. *In any triangle the midpoints of the sides, the feet of the altitudes, and the midpoints of the segments connecting the orthocenter to the vertices, lie on a circle.*

Proof: In Figure 86 the notation on page 139 is used. It will be proved that the circle through A', B', and C', with center at N, also passes through points D, E, F, P, Q, and R. Let AD be any one of the three altitudes. It is sufficient to prove that points P and D are on the circle through A', B', and C'.

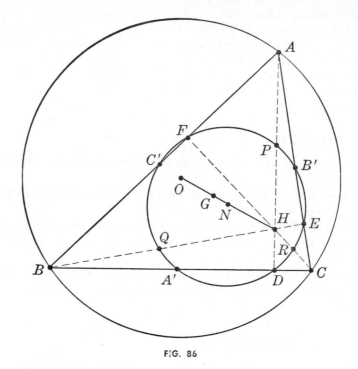

FIG. 86

Point D must lie on the circle through A', B', and C' if $C'A'DB'$ is an isosceles trapezoid. Using well-known properties of lines joining midpoints of sides in a triangle, it follows that sides $C'B'$ and $A'D$ are parallel and that $C'A' = AB'$. Since $B'C'$ is the perpendicular bisector of AD, $AB' = DB'$. Hence $DB' = C'A'$ and quadrilateral $A'DB'C'$ is cyclic.

To prove that P lies on the desired circle it is sufficient to prove that angle $PC'A'$ is a right angle, since the quadrilateral $C'A'DP$, with a right angle at D, is then necessarily cyclic. Since P is the midpoint of AH while C' is the midpoint of AB, $C'P$ is parallel to BH. Since BH is perpendicular to AC and to $A'C'$, angle $PC'A'$ is a right angle.

Theorem 2. *The nine-point circle has its center midway between the orthocenter and the circumcenter, its radius is half the radius of the circumcircle.*

Proof: The point N, Figure 86, is on the perpendicular bisectors of chords $A'D$ and $B'E$. Since each of these bisectors also bisects OH, N is the midpoint of OH.

Triangle $A'B'C'$ is the homothetic image of triangle ABC, with homothetic center G and ratio $-\frac{1}{2}$. The nine-point circle is the image of the circumcircle in the same homothetic transformation so that its radius is half the radius of the circumcircle and points O, G, and N are collinear, with $OG = 2GN$.

The proof of Theorem 2 shows that the points H, N, G, and O are collinear, in the order given, with $2HN = 6NG = 3GO$. The line through these points is called the **Euler line** of the triangle after the great Swiss mathematician, Leonhard Euler, who proved in the eighteenth century that the orthocenter, centroid, and circumcenter are collinear.

Theorem 3. *In a triangle the segment between a vertex and the orthocenter is twice the perpendicular distance from the circumcenter to the opposite side.*

Proof: In Figure 86, the theorem states that $AH = 20A'$. This is proved by showing that $PH = OA'$. Since angle $A'DP$ is a right angle, $A'P$ is a diameter of the nine-point circle and N is the midpoint of $A'P$. Since N is also the midpoint of OH, the diagonals of $OA'HP$ bisect each other and the quadrilateral must be a parallelogram with $PH = OA'$.

Problem 1. *Construct a triangle given one side, the median from the opposite vertex, and the radius of the nine-point circle.*

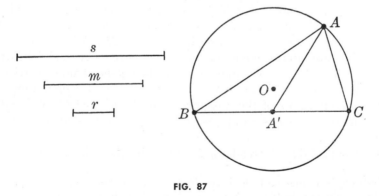

FIG. 87

Construction: In Figure 87, segments of lengths s, m, and r are the given side, median, and radius respectively. Start with a segment BC of length s, and with B and C as centers, swing arcs of radius $2r$ intersecting at O. With O as center and OC as radius, draw the circumcircle of the triangle. With A', the midpoint of BC, as center and m as radius swing an arc cutting the circumcircle at A, the third vertex of the desired triangle.

EXERCISES

1. Prove that an isosceles trapezoid is a cyclic quadrilateral.

2. Prove that the nine-point circle and the circumcircle have the orthocenter as a homothetic center, so that the nine-point circle is the locus of the midpoints of all segments joining the orthocenter to points on the circumcircle.

3. Construct a triangle given the circumcircle, the orthocenter, and one vertex.

4. Construct a triangle given points D, O, and G.

5. Construct a triangle given the circumradius, the distance from the orthocenter to the centroid, and the length of one median.

6. Four points form an *orthocentric group* if each point is the orthocenter of the triangle formed by the other three points. Show that the four triangles, determined by an orthocentric group, have a common nine-point circle.

8.4 INSCRIBED AND ESCRIBED CIRCLES

The following notation is used in this section; most of the notation is illustrated in Figure 88. In triangle ABC, I is the center of the inscribed circle which is tangent to the line segments BC, CA, and AB at the interior points L, M, and N, respectively. The escribed circles have centers at I_1, I_2, and I_3. Circle I_1 is tangent to lines BC, CA, and AB at points L_1, M_1, and N_1; circle I_2 meets these lines in points L_2, M_2, and N_2; circle I_3 meets these lines in points L_3, M_3, and N_3. Points L_1, M_2, and N_3 are interior points of the segments BC, CA, and AB; while points L_2, L_3, M_1, M_3, N_1, and N_2 lie on the extended sides of triangle ABC. The lengths of segments BC, CA, and AB are designated by a, b, and c; the midpoints of these segments are A', B', and C'. The radius of the inscribed circle is r and $s = \frac{1}{2}(a + b + c)$ is the semiperimeter of triangle ABC.

It is assumed that the reader is familiar with the following properties:

Since the two tangents to a circle, drawn from an external point, are equal, numerous segments in Figure 88 are equal; for example, $CM_3 = CL_3$.

The line joining any two of the points I, I_1, I_2, or I_3 bisects either the interior or exterior angle at one vertex of triangle ABC.

From elementary geometry, or trigonometry, it will be recalled that if K is the area of triangle ABC, then $K = rs$.

The lines joining the points of contact of an inscribed or escribed circle to the opposite vertices are concurrent (§ 2.6).

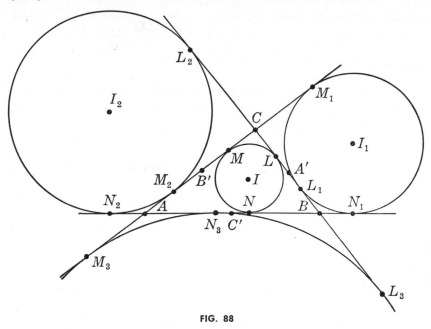

FIG. 88

Any two of the circles shown in Figure 88 have a vertex of triangle ABC as a homothetic center (§ 5.4).

Numerous additional relations concerning lengths of segments shown in Figure 88 are easily derived. The equalities shown in Theorem 1 contain positive segments only and involve segments on side BC. The proofs, and corresponding statements for segments on any side of triangle ABC, are left as exercises.

Theorem 1. *Using notation introduced above*

$$BL_2 = CL_3 = s$$
$$BL_3 = CL_2 = s - a$$
$$CL = s - c, \quad BL = s - b$$
$$L_2L_1 = c, \quad L_2L_3 = b + c$$
$$L_2A' = A'L_3, \quad LA' = A'L_1.$$

Let X, Y, and Z be points, on sides BC, CA, and AB respectively of triangle ABC, for which the Cevian lines AX, BY, and CZ are concurrent and for which perpendiculars to BC, CA, and AB at X, Y, and Z are also concurrent. Let X', Y', and Z' be reflections of X, Y, and Z about A', B', and C', the midpoints of the respective sides. From Theorem 1 of § 2.6, it follows that AX', BY', and CZ' are concurrent and from Theorem 1 of § 4.3, the perpendiculars to BC, CA, and AB at X', Y', and Z' are also concurrent. Since the points of contact of an escribed circle, or of the inscribed circle, satisfy the two theorems just mentioned, use of the equalities in Theorem 1 of the present section gives additional points which satisfy both theorems.

Theorem 2. *Sets of points* (X,Y,Z) *representing points* X, Y, *and* Z *on sides* BC, CA, *and* AB *of triangle* ABC, *so that both*

$$\frac{AZ}{ZB} \cdot \frac{BX}{XC} \cdot \frac{CY}{YA} = +1$$

and

$$(AZ)^2 + (BX)^2 + (CY)^2 = (ZB)^2 + (XC)^2 + (YA)^2$$

include the following combinations of points of contacts of inscribed and escribed circles: (L,M,N), (L_1, M_2, N_3), (L_1, M_1, N_1), (L, M_3, N_2), (L_2, M_2, N_2), (L_3, M, N_1), (L_3, M_3, N_3), *and* (L_2, M_1, N).

EXERCISES

1. In Figure 88, prove that triangles LMN and $I_1 I_2 I_3$ are homothetic.
2. Prove that the area, K, of a triangle is given by $K = rs$.
3. State, in theorem form, a relation for the distance from a vertex of a triangle to a point of contact of the incircle, expressed in terms of lengths of sides of the triangle.
4. Construct a triangle given angle A, side b, and semiperimeter s.
5. Let D be the foot of the altitude from A to side BC of triangle ABC. Does the set (X,Y,Z) in Theorem 2 include points (D, A, A)?

8.5 FEUERBACH'S THEOREM

The theorem considered in this section was first proved by Feuerbach in 1822; since that time numerous proofs have been found. None of the proofs is considered to be simple; most mathematical proofs, however, are composed of relatively simple steps and may not seem complicated to a person with a suitable plan and a good command of background material. It may be noted that the proof given for Feuerbach's theorem mentions inversion, projection, homothetic figures, and reflection.

Theorem 1. *The nine-point circle is tangent to each inscribed and escribed circle.*

Plan of proof: Consider the inscribed circle and an arbitrary one of the escribed circles of a triangle. The sides of the triangle form three common tangents to the two circles. An inversion will be found in which these two circles remain unchanged while the nine-point circle becomes the fourth common tangent to the circles. This will prove that the nine-point circle is tangent to the inscribed circle and to an arbitrary escribed circle and, therefore, is tangent to each escribed circle.

Notation: In Figure 89, I_1 is the center of an arbitrary escribed circle of triangle ABC. Where applicable, the notation of § 8.4 is used. The common internal tangents intersect at point X on I_1I. The fourth tangent line meets circle I_1 at Y, and XY and AC intersect at Z. Point D is the foot of the altitude from A. The line t is tangent to the nine-point circle at point A'.

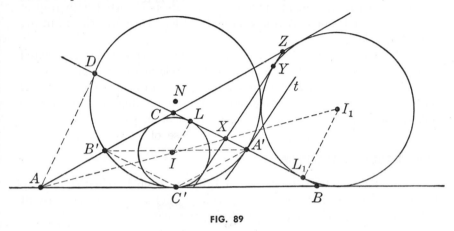

FIG. 89

Proof: Since A' is the midpoint of LL_1, Theorem 1 of § 8.4, the circle with center A' and radius $A'L$ is orthogonal to circles I and I_1. This circle will be used as a circle of inversion. Since circles I and I_1 are unchanged in this inversion, the proof will be completed when it is shown that the inverse image of the nine-point circle is the common tangent XY.

The nine-point circle cuts BC in points A' and D. Since interior and exterior tangents divide the line of centers harmonically, $(AXII_1) = -1$. Lines AD, IL, L_1I_1 are parallel, so that a parallel projection onto line LL_1 gives $(DXLL_1) = -1$. By Theorem 1 of § 7.2, D and X are inverse points in the inversion being considered. Since A' is on the nine-point circle, the image of this circle is a straight line through X, the inverse of point D.

Let β be the angle between $A'C'$ and line t, the tangent to the nine-point circle at A'. Then $\angle A'B'C' = \beta$ since both angles intercept the same arc, $A'C'$, on the nine-point circle. Since triangles $A'B'C'$ and ABC are homothetic, $\angle ABC = \angle A'B'C' = \beta$. Circles I and I_1, along with their common tangents, are symmetric about line I_1I. This means that $\angle CZX = \angle ABC = \beta$. Since AC and $A'C'$ are parallel, t is parallel to XY.

Since angles are preserved in an inversion, the inverse of the nine-point circle must coincide with the common tangent XY.

EXERCISES

1. Discuss Feuerbach's Theorem for the special case in which the given triangle is equilateral.

2. The configuration composed of the inscribed circle, the escribed circles, and the nine-point circle of a triangle is inverted with respect to a circle orthogonal to the escribed circles. Describe the resulting configuration.

3. Refer to Exercise 6, § 8.3, then describe sixteen circles, associated with a triangle, tangent to the nine-point circle of the triangle.

4. Prove directly that the nine-point circle is tangent to two escribed circles by replacing circle I by circle I_2 and making the appropriate changes in Figure 89 and in the proof of Theorem 1.

8.6   PASCAL'S THEOREM

Blaise Pascal (1623–1662) was a brilliant French scientist and inventor; Theorem 1, below, is a special case of a more general result which he discovered when only sixteen years old.

Theorem 1. *If the six points A, B, C, D, E, and F are any points on a circle, the points of intersection of opposite sides of the inscribed hexagon $ABCDEF$ are collinear.*

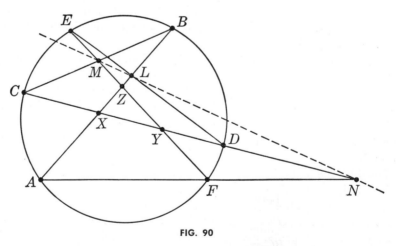

FIG. 90

Proof: In Figure 90, A, B, C, D, E, and F are points on the circumference of a circle. Let AB and DE meet at L, BC and EF meet at M, and CD and FA meet at N. It is to be shown that points L, M, and N are collinear.

Let AB and CD intersect at X, CD and EF intersect at Y, and EF and AB intersect at Z. Apply the Theorem of Menelaus, § 2.5, to triangle XYZ, with successive transversals DE, BC, and FA to obtain

$$\frac{XD}{DY} \cdot \frac{YE}{EZ} \cdot \frac{ZL}{LX} = -1,$$

$$\frac{XC}{CY} \cdot \frac{YM}{MZ} \cdot \frac{ZB}{BX} = -1,$$

$$\frac{XN}{NY} \cdot \frac{YF}{FZ} \cdot \frac{ZA}{AX} = -1.$$

Multiplication of the members of these three equalities, and rearrangement, gives

$$\frac{XN}{NY} \cdot \frac{YM}{MZ} \cdot \frac{ZL}{LX} \cdot \frac{XD \cdot XC}{XB \cdot XA} \cdot \frac{YE \cdot YF}{YC \cdot YD} \cdot \frac{ZB \cdot ZA}{ZE \cdot ZF} = -1.$$

By Theorem 3, § 2.4, each of the last three fractions in this product is equal to 1 so that

$$\frac{XN}{NY} \cdot \frac{YM}{MZ} \cdot \frac{ZL}{LX} = -1$$

and therefore, by the Theorem of Menelaus, points L, M, and N are collinear.

In Figure 90 the line LMN is called the *Pascal Line* of the inscribed hexagon. If the same six concyclic points are assigned the letters A, B, C, D, E, and F in every possible order, sixty distinct Pascal lines may be obtained; sometimes this configuration is called a *mystic hexagram*.

Theorem 1 remains true, when as a limiting case, two consecutive vertices of the inscribed hexagon are coincident and a side of the hexagon is replaced by a line tangent to the circle at this double point. The proof of the special case stated in Theorem 2 is left for the student.

Theorem 2. *In a triangle the intersections of each side with the tangent to the circumcircle at the opposite vertex are collinear.*

Theorem 1, and its several limiting cases, can be useful in solving construction problems without use of a compass. Problem 4 of § 7.8 gave a method for constructing a line tangent to a circle and passing through a given point outside the circle. A special case of Theorem 1 is now used to solve this problem when the given point is on the given circle.

Problem 1. *Construct, without use of a compass, a line tangent to a given circle at a given point on the circle.*

Solution: In Figure 91, E is a given point on the circumference of a given circle. Apply Theorem 1, using the notation of Figure 90, and

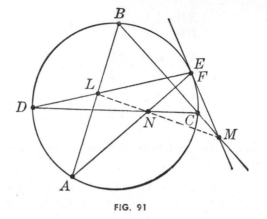

FIG. 91

letting points E and F coincide. Pick points A, B, C, and D, on the given circle, to locate the Pascal line LN. Let BC cut LN at M and draw ME, the desired tangent line.

If the configuration of Figure 90 is transferred onto another plane by a central projection, the circle will, in general, be carried into a conic section that is not a circle; the new hexagon will be "inscribed" in this conic, and the points L, M, and N will remain collinear. This suggests the general form of Pascal's Theorem: *If a hexagon is inscribed in a conic, the points of intersection of opposite sides are collinear.*

From analytic geometry the student should recall that five points, no three collinear, determine a conic. The generalization of Pascal's Theorem provides a method for constructing, with straightedge only, other points on the conic determined by five given points.

The dual of Pascal's Theorem, which is known as *Brianchon's Theorem,* is also true. The student should attempt to dualize Theorem 1, by first replacing six points on a circle by six lines tangent to a circle.

EXERCISES

1. Discuss Pascal's Theorem for a regular hexagon.

2. If six concyclic points are given, show that these points can be joined in sixty ways so that no two of the hexagons formed have the same pairs of opposite sides.

3. Given five points known to be on a circle, construct other points on the circle, using a straightedge only.

4. As a special case of Theorem 1, state a theorem concerning a quadrilateral inscribed in a circle.

5. Find a sixth point on the conic through five given points.

6. In Theorem 2, give information about the location of the Pascal line if the triangle is isosceles or equilateral.

8.7   ISOTOMIC AND ISOGONAL LINES

Definition 1. *Two points on the same side of a triangle are called* **isotomic points** *if the segment joining the points is bisected by the midpoint of the side. Lines joining isotomic points to the opposite vertex are called* **isotomic lines** *and each line is the* **isotomic conjugate** *of the other.*

Theorem 2 of § 2.7 shows that the isotomic conjugates of three concurrent Cevian lines are also concurrent; the two points of concurrency are called **isotomic conjugate points.** The point of intersection of lines joining the vertices of a triangle to points of contact of the inscribed circle is known as the **Gergonne point.** The isotomic conjugate of the Gergonne point is called the **Nagel point.** In Figure 88, lines AL, BM, and CN determine the Gergonne point while the Nagel point lies on lines AL_1, BM_2, and CN_3.

Definition 2. *Two lines through the same vertex of a triangle are called* **isogonal lines** *if the angle between the lines is bisected by the bisector of the given angle; each line is called the* **isogonal conjugate** *of the other.*

Theorem 1. *If three lines, one through each vertex of a triangle, are concurrent, the isogonal conjugate lines are also concurrent.*

Discussion: In Figure 92, let lines AL, BM, and CN intersect at P. If AL', BM', and CN' are the isogonal conjugates of AL, BM, and CN respectively, it is to be shown that AL', BM', and CN' meet in a common point P'. The points P and P' are called **isogonal conjugate points.**

Theorem 1 is conveniently proved by first expressing Ceva's Theorem, § 2.6, in a trigonometric form. In Figure 92, lines AL, BM, and CN are concurrent if and only if

$$\frac{AN}{NB} \cdot \frac{BL}{LC} \cdot \frac{CM}{MA} = 1.$$

By the Law of Sines,

$$\frac{AN}{CA} = \frac{\sin \angle ACN}{\sin \angle CNA}, \quad \text{and} \quad \frac{NB}{BC} = \frac{\sin \angle NCB}{\sin \angle BNC}.$$

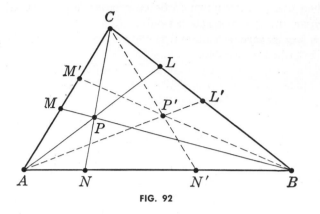

FIG. 92

From these relations, using the fact that $\sin \angle CNA = \sin \angle BNC$, it is easy to show that

$$\frac{AN}{NB} = \frac{CA \sin \angle ACN}{BC \sin \angle NCB}.$$

Likewise,

$$\frac{BL}{LC} = \frac{AB \sin \angle BAL}{CA \sin \angle LAC} \quad \text{and} \quad \frac{CM}{MA} = \frac{BC \sin \angle CBM}{AB \sin \angle MBA}.$$

Substitution yields the following trigonometric form of Ceva's Theorem.

If L, M, and N are points on sides BC, CA, and AB of triangle ABC, lines AL, BM, and CN are concurrent if and only if

$$\frac{\sin \angle ACN}{\sin \angle NCB} \cdot \frac{\sin \angle BAL}{\sin \angle LAC} \cdot \frac{\sin \angle CBM}{\sin \angle MBA} = 1.$$

Since, in Figure 92, lines AL, BM, and CN are concurrent, use of the trigonometric form of Ceva's Theorem, with the substitution of equal angles formed by isogonal lines, shows that lines AL', MB', and CN' are also concurrent.

Definition 3. *The isogonal conjugates of the medians are called the* **symmedians** *of a triangle. The isogonal conjugate of the centroid is known as the* **symmedian point,** *or as the* **Lemoine** *point of the triangle.*

EXERCISES

1. What is the meaning of the prefix "iso" used in words such as *isosceles?*

2. Show that the Gergonne point, Nagel point, and Lemoine point are inside the triangle.

3. State and prove the Law of Sines.

4. Give a trigonometric form for the Theorem of Menelaus.

5. What point of a triangle is a self-isotomic conjugate point? What points are self-isogonal conjugate points?

8.8   THE MIQUEL POINT

The first theorem considered in this section is named for Miquel who gave a proof in 1838, although it is believed that properties associated with this theorem were known before that time.

Theorem 1. *If a point is chosen on each side of a given triangle, the three circles determined by a vertex and the two points on adjacent sides are concurrent.*

Proof: In Figures 93a and 93b, R, S, and T are points on sides BC, CA, and AB, respectively of triangle ABC. Let the circle determined by S, A, and T intersect the circle determined by T, B, and R at point M. The following proof is given for the case in which M is inside triangle ABC, as in Figure 93a. The student should make necessary modifications associated with Figure 93b.

From cyclic quadrilaterals SATM and TBRM, it follows that

$$\angle SMT = 180° - \angle A \quad \text{and} \quad \angle TMR = 180° - \angle B.$$

Since

$$\angle RMS = 360° - \angle SMT - \angle TMR = \angle A + \angle B = 180° - \angle C,$$

it follows, from Theorem 1 of § 2.4, that the circle through R, C, and S must also pass through M.

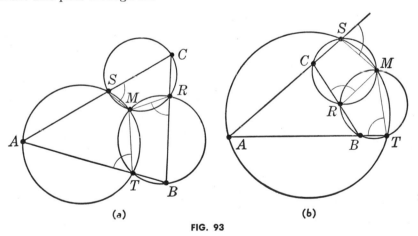

(a)   (b)

FIG. 93

The point M in Figure 93 is known as the **Miquel point** of triangle RST and triangle RST is called a **Miquel triangle** of point M. It is easy to verify that the midpoints of the sides of a triangle have the circumcenter as the Miquel point and that the feet of the altitudes form a Miquel triangle associated with the orthocenter. Indeed, if M is a fixed point in a plane of triangle ABC and perpendiculars from M cut the sides of the triangle in points R, S, and T, then RST is a Miquel triangle of point M.

Theorem 2. *Lines joining the Miquel point to the vertices of a Miquel triangle meet the corresponding sides of the given triangle in equal angles, sense taken into account.*

Proof: The equal angles may be determined by rotating the lines through M counterclockwise about points R, S, and T until they coincide with the respective sides of triangle ABC.

In Figure 93a it is to be proved that $\angle MRB = \angle MSC = \angle MTA$, but in Figure 93b we must show that $\angle MRC = 180° - \angle MSC = \angle MTA$. Since opposite angles of a cyclic quadrilateral are supplementary, these equalities follow.

For a given triangle and a given point as a Miquel point an unlimited number of Miquel triangles are possible. If triangle ABC and point M are given, the choice of R as a point on BC uniquely determines the positions of S and T, on sides CA and AB, so that RST is a Miquel triangle of point M. Each Miquel triangle is, however, similar to every other Miquel triangle having the same Miquel point. This provides a method for solving the problem, mentioned earlier in connection with Problem 3 of § 5.5, of inscribing in a given triangle a triangle which is congruent to a second given triangle.

Theorem 3. *Two triangles are similar if they are inscribed in a given triangle and have the same Miquel point.*

Proof: A triangle will be said to be inscribed in a second one if the vertices of the first are on the sides, or on the extended sides, of the second. In Figure 94, M is the Miquel point both of triangle RST and of triangle $R'S'T'$. By Theorem 2, $\angle CRM = \angle BTM = 180° - \angle ASM$ and $\angle CR'M = \angle BT'M = \angle AS'M$. It is immediately evident that triangles RMR', TMT', and SMS' are similar. Hence in a rotation, through angle RMR' about M, followed by an expansion about M, of order $k = MR'/MR$, the images of R, S, and T are R', S', and T' respectively. Since angles are preserved in this combined transformation, triangles RST and $R'S'T'$ are similar.

Problem 1. *Let triangles ABC and XYZ be given. Locate point R on BC, point S on CA, and point T on AB so that triangles RST and XYZ are congruent.*

Solution: The given triangles are shown in Figure 94. As in Problem 3 of § 5.5, construct triangle $R'S'T'$ homothetic to XYZ, with vertices

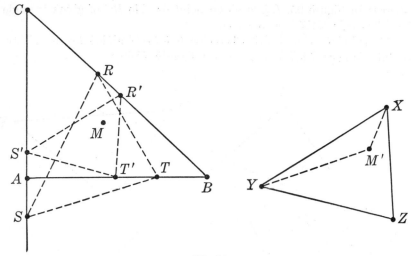

FIG. 94

on the proper sides of triangle ABC. Find M, the Miquel point of triangle $R'S'T'$. Locate M' in triangle XYZ so that triangles $S'MR'$ and $YM'X$ are similar. With M as center and $M'Y$ as radius, swing an arc cutting AC at S. With S as center and YZ and YX as radii, the desired points T and R may be located on AB and BC.

There are none, one, or two solutions depending on the number of times the arc with center M and radius $M'Y$ cuts line AC.

Theorem 4. *Two similar triangles inscribed in the same triangle have the same Miquel point.*

The proof is left as an exercise.

Theorem 5. *If a variable polygon moves so that it remains similar to a given polygon and if three vertices move on three given lines, then each vertex moves on a line.*

Proof: For different positions of the variable polygon, the three vertices which move on given lines determine similar triangles which are inscribed in the triangle formed by the given lines. By Theorem 4 all these similar triangles have a common Miquel point, which is a fixed point in the combined rotation and expansion that carries one polygon into another similar one. By Theorem 3 of § 5.6, if one vertex of the variable polygon traces a straight line each vertex must trace a straight line.

Problem 2. *In a given triangle inscribe a triangle similar to a second given triangle with one vertex at a given point.*

Given: In Figure 95, L is a given point on side BC of given triangle ABC. Triangle XYZ is also given.

To find: Points M and N are to be located on CA and AB respectively, so that triangles XYZ and LMN are directly similar.

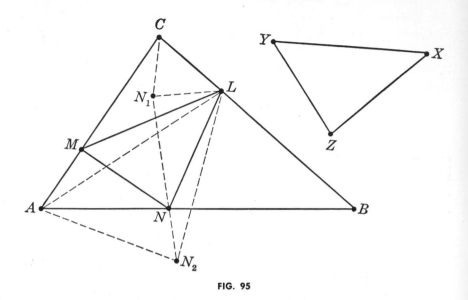

FIG. 95

First solution: Construct points N_1 and N_2 so that triangles LCN_1 and LAN_2 are directly similar to triangle XYZ. Let line N_1N_2 cut AB at N. If point M is constructed so that triangles XYZ and LMN are directly similar, M will fall on CA. The construction was made by an application of Theorem 3 of § 5.6 which shows that if L is fixed, and triangle LMN moves so that it remains similar to XYZ with M moving on CA, then N must move on line N_1N_2.

Second solution: As in Problem 3, § 5.5, locate points L', M', and N' on BC, CA, and AB so that triangles $L'M'N'$ and XYZ are homothetic. Locate P, the Miquel point of triangle $L'M'N'$. Rotate triangle $L'M'N'$ through angle $L'PL$ about P and follow by an expansion of order $k = PL/PL'$, to obtain the desired triangle LMN.

Problem 3. *In a given quadrilateral, inscribe a quadrilateral similar to a second given quadrilateral.*

Discussion: Theorem 5 provides a method for solving this problem. Suppose that points P, Q, R, and S are to be located on sides AB, BC, CD, and DA of a given quadrilateral $ABCD$ so that $PQRS$ is similar to a second given quadrilateral, say $EFGH$.

Pick a point P_1 on AB and, as in Problem 2, find points Q_1 and R_1 on BC and CD so that triangles $P_1 Q_1 R_1$ and EFG are similar. Construct S_1 so that quadrilaterals $P_1 Q_1 R_1 S_1$ and $EFGH$ are similar. In a like manner, construct quadrilateral $P_2 Q_2 R_2 S_2$, similar to $EFGH$, with P_2, Q_2, and R_2 on AB, BC, and CD.

Let the line $S_1 S_2$ cut DA at point S. As in Problem 2, construct points R and P on sides CD and AB so that triangles RSP and GHE are similar. If Q is now constructed so that triangles PQR and EFG are similar, Q lies on BC and $PQRS$ is the desired quadrilateral.

EXERCISES

1. If M is a common point of intersection of three circles which also intersect, two at a time, in points R, S, and T, show that an unlimited number of triangles have RST as a Miquel triangle of point M and that all of these triangles are similar.

2. Apply Theorem 3, § 5.6, to inscribe in a given triangle a triangle similar to a second given one, with one side passing through a given point.

3. Given four lines, locate a point on each line so that the points are vertices of a square.

4. The sides of a complete quadrilateral determine four triangles. Prove that the circumcircles of these triangles are concurrent. The point of intersection is called the Miquel point of the quadrilateral.

5. Prove that the perpendiculars from the Miquel point (Exercise 4) of a complete quadrilateral meet the sides in four collinear points. The line through these points is the Simson line of the quadrilateral.

REVIEW EXERCISES

1. Use the trigonometric form of the Theorem of Ceva to show that bisectors of the interior angles of a triangle are concurrent.

2. Show that the centroid, orthocenter, circumcenter, and nine-point center of a triangle, when arranged in proper order, form a harmonic range.

3. Construct a circle, of a given coaxal system, orthogonal to a given circle.

4. Construct a triangle given the circumcircle and the nine-point center. How many solutions exist?

5. Prove the limiting points of a non-intersecting coaxal system, § 8.2, divide the diameter of each circle of the system harmonically.

6. Given collinear points A, B, C, and D, locate points E and F so that $(ABEF) = -1$ and $(DCEF) = -1$. Do real points E and F always exist?

7. Prove that the circumcircle and the nine-point circle, of an obtuse triangle, are inverse circles with respect to the self-polar circle of the triangle.

8. In a square inscribe a rectangle whose base is twice its altitude.

9. Theorem 4, § 2.4, shows that perpendiculars to the sides of a triangle, from a point on the circumcircle, meet the sides in points on a line called the Simson line. Explain how the Simson line is a limiting case of the Miquel triangle of a point on the circumcircle.

10. Prove this generalization of Theorem 4, § 2.4. Lines drawn to the sides of a triangle from a point on the circumcircle, meeting the sides in equal angles sense taken into account, determine collinear points on the sides of the triangle.

★11. Show that an unlimited number of squares may be inscribed in a given square. Can any square be inscribed in a rectangle that is not a square?

★12. Prove that the radical axis of the circles

$$x^2 + y^2 + ax + by + c = 0 \quad \text{and} \quad x^2 + y^2 + dx + ey + f = 0$$

is $(a - d) x + (b - e) y + (c - f) = 0$. Give a geometric interpretation of the usual process of finding the co-ordinates of the points of intersection of two given circles, including circles with no real points of intersection.

★13. Given the triangle with vertices $(0,0)$, $(6,0)$, and $(4,3)$, find the co-ordinates of the centroid, orthocenter, circumcenter, and nine-point circle. Is the incenter on the Euler line?

9

A Problem of Steiner

~~~~~~

9.1 INTRODUCTION

Each remaining chapter contains a discussion in which elementary material (or a topic previously discussed) is extended to a more general result. Since these discussions are independent of each other, the following chapters may be studied (or omitted) in any order. Some instructors may chose to assign this material, or associated problems, for special reports.

The problem of Apollonius (see § 6.4) is often called the most famous problem of elementary geometry. A generalization, known as the *problem of Steiner*, is the problem of constructing a circle cutting three given circles at three given angles. Several special cases of Steiner's problem were considered in Chapter 6; in particular, the student should recall a method for constructing a circle passing through a given point and cutting two given circles in specified angles (Problem 1, § 6.6).

The present discussion is intended to show, in a fairly direct manner, how the problem of Steiner can be solved, without attempting to discuss special cases or the number of solutions. As in Definition 1 of § 6.5, the angle between two intersecting circles is the smaller angle between lines tangent to the circles at a point of intersection (or 90° if the tangent lines are perpendicular). The method of solution is essentially that given by Coolidge,* who defines the angle between circles in a different manner.

9.2 A BASIC THEOREM

We first disregard one of the given conditions in Steiner's problem and study the family of all circles cutting two given circles at two given angles. When the given circles are mutually external, we already know

---

* J. L. Coolidge, *A Treatise on the Circle and the Sphere* (Oxford, 1916), p. 167.

how to construct four lines which cut the circles at the desired angles (Problem 3, § 6.5).

In Figure 96, let A and B be given mutually external circles and let α and β be given angles not greater than 90°. We wish to study the family of all circles that intersect A at the angle α and B at the angle β. Let lines x, y, z, and w cut circle A in angle α and circle B in angle β. Let

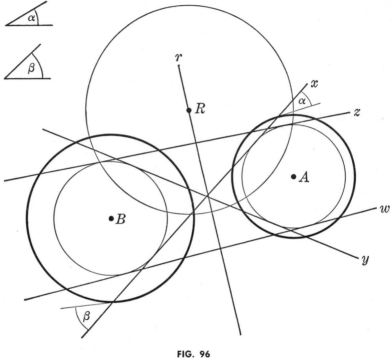

FIG. 96

the line r be the radical axis (§ 8.1) of circles A and B. Let R be an arbitrary point on the radical axis and construct the circle, with center R, orthogonal to both of the circles A and B.

If the circle R is now used as a circle of inversion, circles A and B remain unchanged (Theorem 2, § 6.6) while the image of each of the lines x, y, z, and w is a circle which intersects circle A in angle α and circle B in angle β (Theorem 1 of § 6.6).

In Figure 97, circle A, circle B, line r, angle α, angle β, and line y are identical with the corresponding elements in Figure 96. Let K be any circle which cuts circle A in angle α and circle B in angle β. Let circle K cut r in points X and Y. Construct the circle X, with center at X, which is orthogonal to circles A and B.

Now invert the elements of Figure 97 with respect to circle X. In this inversion line r, circle A, and circle B remain unchanged; the inverse of circle K is the line y which cuts circle A in angle α and circle B in angle β. Let θ be the angle in which line r intersects circle K. Since the magnitude of an angle is preserved in inversion, lines r and y also intersect in angle θ.

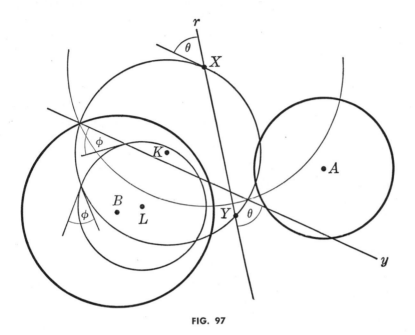

FIG. 97

In Figure 97, let circle L be an arbitrary member of the coaxal system of circles determined by circles A and B. Circle X, which is orthogonal to circles A and B, must also be orthogonal to circle L (Theorem 1, § 8.2). Let circles L and K intersect in angle ϕ; then line y also cuts circle L in angle ϕ because, in the inversion with respect to circle X, circle L is fixed but line y is the inverse of circle K.

We may also invert the configuration of Figure 97 with respect to the circle, with center at Y, orthogonal to circles A, B, and L. In this inversion circle K becomes a line, say x, cutting circle A in angle α, cutting circle B in angle β, and cutting circle L in angle ϕ. (Line x, which is not shown in Figure 97, may be obtained by reflecting y about line AB.)

Hence, in Figure 96, the family of circles obtained by inverting line y, with respect to all circles with center on r and orthogonal to circles A and B, coincides with the family of circles obtained by inverting line x

in this manner. A second and different family of circles is obtained by similar inversion either of line z or of line w.

Theorem 1. *Let a fixed line cut two given circles at two given angles. Let a third circle, which cuts the given circles at the given angles, be such that it can be inverted into the line when the circle of inversion is orthogonal to the two given circles and has its center at an intersection of the third circle with the radical axis of the given circles. Then any circle, coaxal with the two given circles, which cuts the third circle will cut the line and the third circle in equal angles.*

Discussion: The statement of Theorem 1 can be simplified by a revision of the definition of the angle of intersection of two circles, or of a line and a circle (see Coolidge).* This theorem, which summarizes results obtained above, provides a method for changing the original problem of Steiner into other forms. For example, if we find a circle coaxal with circles A and B, Figure 97, and tangent to line y, this circle must also be tangent to circle K. If we can find three circles which must be tangent to a circle which solves the problem of Steiner, we will have reduced the problem to the related problem of finding a particular solution of the problem of Apollonius.

9.3 A PRELIMINARY PROBLEM

Problem 1. *Given two circles and a line, construct a circle coaxal with the given circles and tangent to the given line.*

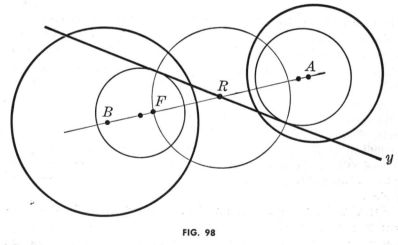

FIG. 98

* Coolidge, *op. cit.*, pp. 108–109.

First we shall assume that the given circles are neither concentric nor intersecting. Let the given circles have centers A and B and let the given line be y, Figure 98. Let the radical axis of circles A and B cut line AB at R. Construct the circle with center at R, orthogonal to both of the circles A and B. By Theorem 1 of § 8.2, any circle with center on line AB, orthogonal to circle R, will belong to the coaxal system determined by circles A and B. Hence the given problem is equivalent to a special case of Steiner's problem; we wish to construct a circle orthogonal to circle R, orthogonal to line AB, and tangent to line y.

Let F be one point of intersection of line AB and circle R. With F as center and with any convenient radius, invert the configuration. Line AB remains fixed; circle R becomes a straight line perpendicular to AB, say at point G; line y becomes a circle, through F but not through G unless y passes through the second intersection of AB and circle R.

We now construct a circle with center at G (and hence orthogonal to all lines through G) tangent to the circle obtained by inverting line y. This elementary problem usually has two solutions and re-inversion gives solutions for the original problem.

The above solution is not valid if the two given circles intersect. In this case, however, the problem reduces to a familiar one (Problem 1, § 3.2) of finding a circle passing through two points (the intersections of the given circles) and tangent to a given line.

9.4 STEINER'S PROBLEM, GENERAL SOLUTION

Problem 1. *Construct a circle meeting three given circles in three given angles.*

Solution: In Figure 99, circles A, B, and C and angles α, β, and γ are given. We wish to construct a circle which cuts circle A in angle α, circle B in angle β, and circle C in angle γ.

First construct a line y cutting circle A in angle α and cutting circle B in angle β (Problem 3, § 6.5). Then construct a line p cutting circle A in angle α and cutting circle C in angle γ. Apply Problem 1 of § 9.3 to construct the two circles which are both coaxal with circles A and C and also tangent to line p. Likewise construct the two circles coaxal with circles A and B and tangent to line y.

A solution of Problem 1 may be found by constructing a circle tangent (in the proper manner) to three of these new circles. Selecting the appropriate solution of the Problem of Apollonius is simplified by noting that the circle must also be tangent to the fourth of the constructed coaxal circles. In Figure 99, the circle with center D cuts circle A in angle α, cuts circle B in angle β, and cuts circle C in angle γ. Note that circle D may be inverted into line y and also into line p in the manner described in Theorem 1 of § 9.2.

In Figure 99, line q cuts circles B and C in angles β and γ. (Whether q should cut the segment BC internally or externally depends upon the positions of lines y and p.) The two circles coaxal with circles B and C and tangent to line q have also been constructed. The solution circle, with center at D, is tangent to all six of the circles coaxal with pairs of the original circles.

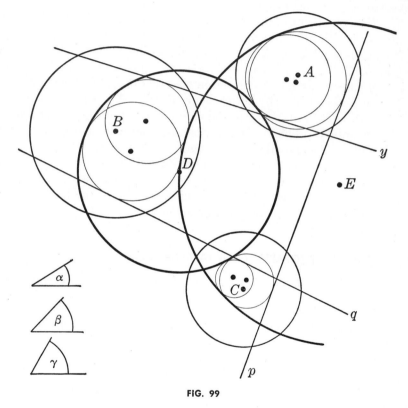

FIG. 99

Now let us invert the configuration with respect to the circle orthogonal to circles A, B, and C. This circle must also be orthogonal to each of the six new circles so that nine of the circles shown in Figure 99 remain unchanged. Circle D, however, becomes a new circle with center at point E. Since this circle cuts circles A, B, and C in angles α, β, and γ, respectively, it also is a solution to Problem 1.

9.5   A SPECIAL CASE

The given circles in Steiner's problem may, as limiting cases, be replaced either by lines or by points; we shall now discuss the solution of a
special problem of this type.

Problem 1. *Construct a circle which meets three given lines at three*
specified angles.

Solution: By inversion, the three given lines may be changed into
three circles; the problem is then identical with Problem 1 of § 9.4. We
shall, however, solve this special problem without using the inversion
transformation.*

In Figure 100, lines p, q, and r and angles P, Q, and R are given. We
wish to construct a circle cutting lines p, q, and r at angles P, Q, and R,
respectively. With an arbitrary center, O', and any convenient radius
draw a circle. Now construct lines p', q', and r' parallel to lines p, q,
and r, cutting circle O' at angles P, Q, and R, respectively.

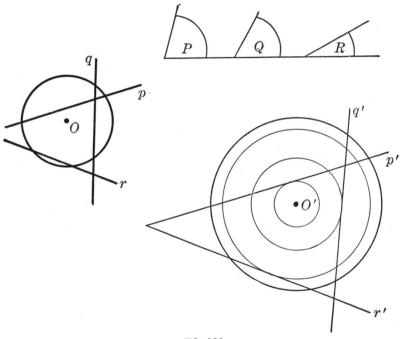

FIG. 100

* This solution is essentially that given by Jose Padro in a Master's thesis, *An*
Extension of the Problem of Apollonius, Ohio State University (1950).

We complete a solution by constructing the circle with center O so that the configuration consisting of the circle O and lines p, q, and r is homothetic (§ 5.4) to the configuration composed of circle O' and lines p', q', and r'.

Since two lines, parallel to a given line, cut a given circle in a given angle (different from 90°), there are, in general, eight distinct solutions. If the given lines are concurrent (or parallel) there may be no solution since the directions of the concurrent lines and the magnitudes of the three angles of intersection are not completely independent of each other. If one solution exists, for this special case, there are an unlimited number of solutions; any circle homothetic to a solution circle, with the point of concurrency as homothetic center, will also be a solution.

REVIEW EXERCISES

1. Is the solution given for Problem 1 of § 9.3 valid when one of the given circles is inside the second circle?

2. Construct a circle cutting the sides of an equilateral triangle at angles of 0°, 45°, and 90°.

3. Construct a circle coaxal with two given circles and orthogonal to a third given circle.

4. If three circles have equal radii, prove that any circle, having its center at the radical center, cuts the three circles at the same angle.

5. Apply the result of Exercise 4 to construct a circle cutting three given circles at the same given angle.

6. Outline a method for constructing a circle passing through a given point, cutting a given circle at an angle of 45°, and cutting a given line at an angle of 30°. Is a solution possible if the point and the circle lie on opposite sides of the given line?

7. It is possible to construct a circle cutting each of four given circles at the same angle. For a solution see Coolidge, *A Treatise on the Circle and the Sphere* (Oxford, 1916), p. 174.

10

Generalization of a Quadrilateral Construction Problem

10.1 SQUARES THROUGH FOUR POINTS

In Figure 101, let lines a, b, c, and d form the sides of the square $WXYZ$. Now pick points A on a, B on b, C on c, and D on d; the points

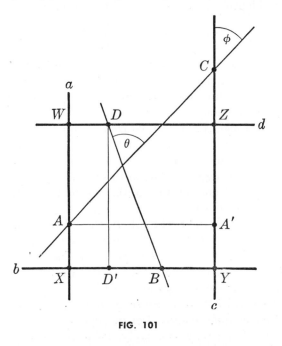

FIG. 101

may be either on the segments WX, XY, YZ, and ZW or on the extended sides of $WXYZ$. If the sides and vertices of $WXYZ$ are now erased, leaving points A, B, C, and D, can we reconstruct the square?

After making an analysis which shows that a solution is possible, we shall arrive at a simple method of construction.

Problem 1. *Given four points, construct a line through each point so that the lines form the sides of a square.*

Analysis: In Figure 101, let points A, B, C, and D be given. We wish to find lines a, b, c, and d through A, B, C, and D respectively, so that these lines form a square. Let us assume that we have a solution in which A and C are on opposite sides of the square. Methods of numerical trigonometry suggest using the lengths of line segments AC and BD and the magnitude of θ, the angle between AC and BD. Let ϕ be the angle between AC and side c of the desired square. Is ϕ determined by AC, BD, and θ?

Let perpendiculars from A and D cut the opposite sides of the desired square in points A' and D'. In triangle $AA'C$ we have $AA' = AC \sin \phi$. In triangle $D'DB$, angle $D'DB = \theta - \phi$, so that $DD' = DB \cos (\theta - \phi)$. If $WXYZ$ is a square, segments AA' and DD' must be equal in magnitude. It follows that $AC \sin \phi = \pm DB \cos (\theta - \phi)$ and, by familiar trigonometric identities, this is changed to the form

$$\cot \phi = \frac{\pm AC - BD \sin \theta}{BD \cos \theta}.$$

From this formula we may obtain: (a) a method for constructing angle ϕ; (b) information about the number of solutions; and (c) special locations of the given points which affect the number of solutions.

When $\phi = 0°$, no solution exists, with A and C on opposite sides, since the sides through A and C must coincide for this case. The formula for $\cot \phi$ shows that $\phi = 0°$ only when $\theta = 90°$. If, however, AC and BD are equal in magnitude when $\theta = 90°$, $\cot \phi$ is indeterminate for one choice of signs. This suggests that, in this case, an unlimited number of solutions may exist. Consideration of this possibility leads to the following solution for Problem 1.

Construction (first method): Let A, B, C, and D be the given points in Figure 102. Through B erect a line perpendicular to AC and on this line locate point P so that $AC = BP$. Draw PD and through B construct a line parallel to PD. Complete the square $XYZW$ by drawing lines perpendicular to PD through points A and C.

Proof: Clearly $XYZW$ is a rectangle and we need only prove that XY and YZ have equal lengths. Let perpendiculars from A and B cut YZ and ZW at A' and B', respectively. Then triangles $AA'C$ and $BB'P$ are similar, since corresponding sides are perpendicular; and the triangles are also congruent, since $AC = BP$. It follows that $AA' = BB'$, so that

$XYZW$ is a square. (Note that this construction and proof could be presented in the early part of a beginning geometry course.)

Number of solutions: First assume, as in the given construction, that AC and BD are not perpendicular. Since PB is not a directed segment, there are two locations for P on the perpendicular to AC through B. Since the construction and proof is valid in each case, there are at least two solution squares having A and C on opposite sides.

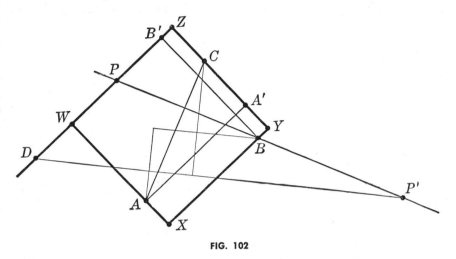

FIG. 102

Suppose we have any solution square, with A and C on opposite sides; the side through D must cut line BP in some point, say P''. Now let perpendiculars from A and B cut the opposite sides of this new square in points A'' and B''. Since triangles $AA''C$ and $BB''P''$ are congruent, $BP'' = AC = BP$ and the solution square coincides with one of the two obtained by our construction method. Therefore, if AC and BD are not perpendicular, only two solutions exist for A and C on opposite sides of the square.

Since Problem 1 has solutions for A and B on opposite sides and for A and D on opposite sides, there are, in general, six distinct solutions. (These correspond to the six essentially different seating arrangements of four persons at a bridge table.)

If, see Figure 102, P and D coincide, there are an unlimited number of solutions of one type. If points B, P, and D are distinct collinear points, there is no solution with A and C on opposite sides of the square. Problem 1 has constructible solutions except for the special case in which the points A, B, C, and D form a triangle and its orthocenter. (For this case all solutions have degenerated into three points, the feet of the altitudes of the triangle determined by three of the given points in the orthocentric group.)

Second analysis and construction: In Figure 103, let $XYZW$ be a square with sides passing through the points A, B, C, and D. One locus for vertex X is the circle having AB as diameter; likewise, Z is on the circle with CD as diameter. Let line XZ again intersect these circles at points M and N, respectively. Since $\angle AXM = \angle DZN = 45°$, M and N lie on the perpendicular bisectors of AB and CD. This analysis sug-

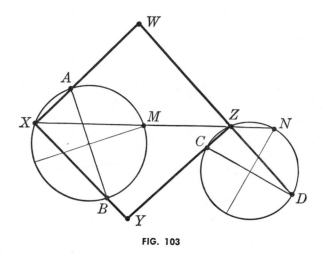

FIG. 103

gests a second solution for Problem 1. (The student may attempt to verify that M will be to the left of directed segment AB and N to the left of directed segment CD if the points A, B, C, and D are on the sides of the square in counterclockwise order.) Line MN cuts the constructed circles in points X and Z which are vertices of the desired solution square.

EXERCISES

1. Solve Problem 1 if the given points are collinear.

2. Draw a square having lines a, b, c, and d as consecutive sides, in counterclockwise order. Draw a second square with lines a', b', c', and d' as consecutive sides, in counterclockwise order. Let lines a and a' intersect at A, b and b' intersect at B, c and c' intersect at C, and d and d' intersect at D. Find additional relations connecting the points A, B, C, and D.

3. Construct a rectangle similar to a given one, with each side passing through one of four given points. How many solutions are possible?

4. Exercise 3 is one generalization of Problem 1; suggest other possible generalizations.

5. In Figure 103, let M and N be either of the two points in which perpendicular bisectors of AB and CD cut the circles having these segments as diameters. Verify that these choices lead to four different solutions of Problem 1.

10.2 SIMILAR QUADRILATERALS THROUGH FOUR POINTS

The remaining sections of this chapter contain generalizations of Problem 1 of § 10.1 and discussions of related problems. For the first generalization we shall replace the square by a general quadrilateral.

Problem 1. *Given four points and a quadrilateral, construct a line through each point so that the lines form a quadrilateral similar to the given one.*

First analysis and construction: In Figure 104, quadrilateral $X'Y'Z'W'$ and the points A, B, C, and D are given. We wish to construct a quadrilateral $XYZW$, similar to $X'Y'Z'W'$, with A on WX, B on XY, C on YZ, and D on ZW. We shall generalize the second construction used

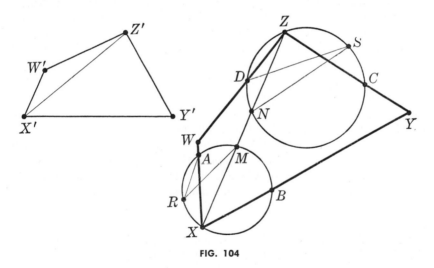

FIG. 104

for Problem 1 of § 10.1. In that problem we used the fact that the diagonal of a square meets the sides in angles of 45 degrees; now we draw diagonal $X'Z'$ of the given quadrilateral and note that the angles in which the diagonal XZ meets the sides of quadrilateral $XYZW$ are determined.

Construct the circle through A and B so that the arc, on the right side of the directed segment AB, contains the given angle $W'X'Y'$, Theorem 2 of § 4.1. Also construct the circle through C and D so that angle $Y'Z'W'$ is inscribed in the arc on the right side of segment CD. Let R be any point on the arc to the right of AB and construct angle ARM, equal to angle $W'X'Z'$, and with M on arc AB. Likewise, pick S on the arc to the right of CD and locate N on arc CD so that angle DSN is equal to angle $W'Z'X'$. Draw MN cutting the circles again in points X and Z as shown. Let XA and DZ intersect at W and let XB and ZC intersect at Y to complete the required quadrilateral $XYZW$.

To prove that the quadrilaterals $XYZW$ and $X'Y'Z'W'$ are similar we note that, by construction, each angle in triangle XWZ is equal to the corresponding angle in triangle $X'W'Z'$ and that each angle in triangle XZY is equal to the corresponding angle in triangle $X'Z'Y'$.

A particular solution of Problem 1 can be specified by designating which side of $XYZW$ is to pass through each of the given points. The problem has 24 solutions if $XYZW$ is directly similar to $X'Y'Z'W'$, 48 if inversely similar quadrilaterals are allowed. For the particular arrangement of the given points on the sides of $WXYZ$ as shown in Figure 104, only one solution is possible unless points M and N coincide; if M and N do coincide there are an unlimited number of solutions.

Second analysis: In our first solution of the square problem, see Figure 102, we located a point P so that every square, with A, B, and C on consecutive sides, had its fourth side passing through P. This method may also be extended to give a solution for the quadrilateral problem.

Let us draw any convenient line a through A, Figure 105, then construct a line b through B meeting a in angle $W'X'Y'$. Next construct a line c through C meeting b in angle $X'Y'Z'$, preserving the order of the angles in $X'Y'Z'W'$. Finally, construct line d so that the lines a, b, c, and d form a quadrilateral $WXYZ$ similar to $W'X'Y'Z'$. Now start with a second line a' through A and repeat these steps to obtain a second quadrilateral, similar to $W'X'Y'Z'$, with fourth side d'. Let d and d' intersect at P so that two distinct quadrilaterals similar to $W'X'Y'Z'$ have their corresponding sides passing through the points A, B, C, and P.

Let the line XZ cut the circle through A, B, and X at M. Construct the circle through C, P, and Z; then let XZ cut this circle at N. From the first solution of this problem (compare Figure 104), it follows that points M and N must coincide, since two distinct quadrilaterals similar to $W'X'Y'Z'$ have corresponding sides passing through points A, B, C, and P. Note that the position of point P, the intersection of d and d', is uniquely determined by the given quadrilateral $W'X'Y'Z'$, the given

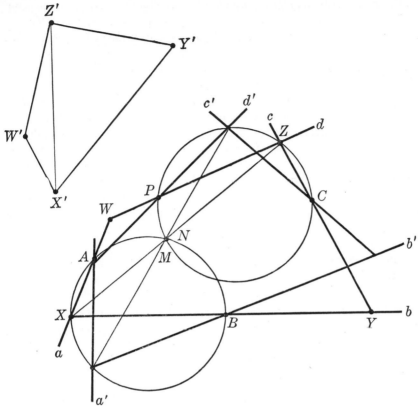

FIG. 105

points A, B, and C, and the order in which corresponding sides of $WXYZ$ are to pass through the given points. In Figure 105, P must lie both on the circle through points M, C, and Z and on the line through Z which meets MZ in angle $X'Z'W'$.

To solve Problem 1 we may ignore the given point D until we have located point P as indicated in the previous discussion. Then line PD is one side of the desired quadrilateral; we complete the construction by drawing lines through A, B, and C meeting PD in the proper angles, determined by $W'X'Y'Z'$.

In making the above analysis we have provided the essential steps needed to prove the following theorem. A different proof is given by Petersen.*

---

* Julius Petersen, *Methods and Theories for the Solution of Problems of Geometrical Constructions Applied to 410 Problems* (Copenhagen, Andr. Fred. Host and Son, 1879), p. 76.

Theorem 1. *If a polygon, which remains similar to a given polygon, moves in such a manner that three lines of the polygon each pass through fixed points, then each line of the polygon must pass through a fixed point.*

EXERCISES

1. Using the notation of Figure 105, let $W'X'Y'Z'$ be a rectangle with $W'X' = 2X'Y'$. Is PB perpendicular to AC and does $PB = 2AC$?

2. Solve Problem 1 if $W'X'Y'Z'$ (Figure 105) is a rhombus with $\angle W'X'Y' = 45°$. Are segments PB and AC equal? Does PB cut AC in an angle of $45°$?

3. In Figure 105, Problem 1 has an unlimited number of solutions (with A on WX, B on XY, C on YZ, and D on ZW) if points D and P coincide. Where can D be located so that no solution of this type is possible?

4. Construct a quadrilateral similar to a given one with three sides passing through given points and with the fourth side tangent to a given circle.

10.3   SQUARES WITH SIDES TANGENT TO FOUR CIRCLES

We again consider generalizations of Problem 1 of § 10.1; in § 10.2 we replaced the original square by a quadrilateral; now we replace the given points by circles and then construct a square so that each side is tangent to a different one of four given circles. A key to a solution is provided by the conjecture, suggested by Theorem 1 of § 10.2, that if a square moves continuously so that three sides remain tangent to fixed circles, then the fourth side may also remain tangent to a fixed circle.

Problem 1. *Given four circles construct lines tangent to each circle so that the lines form the sides of a square.*

Analysis and construction: In Figure 106 let $XYZW$ be a square with vertices X, Y, Z, W in consecutive counterclockwise order. Let the circles with centers A, B, C, D and radii a, b, c, d be tangent to lines WX, XY, YZ, ZW at points A', B', C', D' respectively. Through points A, B, and C construct lines parallel to WX, XY, and YZ; then construct a fourth line so that these lines form the square $W'X'Y'Z'$, with A, B, and C on consecutive sides in counterclockwise order. Let the line through B, perpendicular to AC, cut $W'Z'$ at P. As in the second solution of Problem 1 of § 10.1, $BP = AC$. Let the line through P, perpendicular to ZW, cut ZW at P'. Then, for the particular arrangement of circles shown in Figure 106,

$$XY = X'Y' - A'A + C'C = X'Y' - a + c.$$

Likewise,
$$YZ = Y'Z' + B'B - P'P = Y'Z' + b - P'P.$$
Using the equalities $XY = YZ$ and $X'Y' = Y'Z'$, we obtain the result
$$P'P = a + b - c.$$

If, in Figure 106, the square $XYZW$ moves continuously so that sides WX, XY, and YZ remain tangent to circles A, B, and C, it follows that side ZW will remain tangent to a circle whose center is at the point P and whose radius is the absolute value of $a + b - c$.

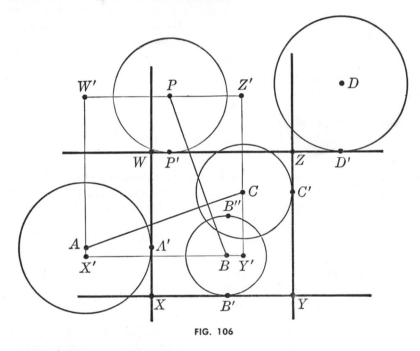

FIG. 106

Given circles A, B, C, and D, we may solve Problem 1 by locating point P so that segments AC and BP are both equal and perpendicular. (The point P has two possible positions; one will give solutions with A, B, C, D on consecutive sides in clockwise order, the other gives counterclockwise order.) We then construct the circle with center P and with a radius p given by $p = |a \pm b \pm c|$. (The four different choices of signs lead to solutions with different types of tangency. For example, if in Figure 106 we let WX be tangent to circle A at A', XY be tangent to circle B at B'' where $B'B''$ is a diameter of B, and YZ be tangent to circle C at C', $p = |a - b - c|$.)

Finally we construct a common tangent to circles P and D to obtain one side, ZW, of the desired square. The solution is completed by constructing a line tangent to circle B and parallel to ZW, then by constructing lines tangent to circles A and C and perpendicular to ZW. Each of the lines tangent to circles B, A, and C must, however, be the correct one of the two possible tangents having the proper direction.

Since, in Figure 106, circles P and D do not intersect, four common tangents may be drawn and each leads to a solution of Problem 1. It is possible to complete these additional solutions by visualizing a continuous variation of square $XYZW$, with sides remaining tangent to circles A, B, C, and D, until WZ is tangent to circle D at a point other than D'. Complete directions for each step in any desired solution are contained in a master's thesis by Louis L. Ross.* Although 96 different solutions for Problem 1 are possible, some may not exist; in Figure 106, some solutions vanish if circles P and D intersect.

Taken together, Problems 1 of §§ 10.2 and 10.3 suggest the following more general problem.

Problem 2. *Given four circles and a quadrilateral, construct a line tangent to each of the circles so that the lines form a quadrilateral similar to the given one.*

Following the development of § 10.2, let us consider a quadrilateral which moves in such a way that the quadrilateral remains similar to a given one and each of three sides remains tangent to one of three given circles. Under these conditions, will the fourth side of the quadrilateral also remain tangent to a fixed circle? A proof that the answer is "yes" is contained in a master's thesis by Harold Brockman.† Although a proof will not be given here, the student should note that a proof provides a method for solving Problem 2 and gives the following extension of Theorem 1 of § 10.2.

Theorem 1. *If a polygon, which remains similar to a given polygon, moves in such a manner that three lines of the polygon remain tangent to three fixed circles, then each line of the polygon must remain tangent to a fixed circle.*

EXERCISES

1. In Figure 106, let circles A, B, and C be excircles of a given equilateral triangle and D be the corresponding incircle. Solve Problem 1 for this configuration.

2. Construct a square so that the first side is tangent to a given circle,

---

* Louis Leo Ross, *Extensions and Applications of a Geometrical Construction Problem* (Ohio State University, 1949).

† Harold W. Brockman, *Geometric Transformations* (Ohio State University, 1950).

the second and third sides (in counterclockwise order) pass through given points, and the fourth side has a given direction.

10.4 RELATED PROBLEMS

The solution of Problem 3 of § 8.8 describes a method for inscribing a quadrilateral similar to a given one in a second given quadrilateral. This is related to the material considered in the present chapter and a different solution will be presented.

Problem 1. *Locate points on each of four given lines so that the points are the vertices of a quadrilateral similar to a given one.*

Solution: In Figure 107, let $ABCD$ be the given quadrilateral and let a, b, c, and d be the given lines. Let a and b intersect at X, b and c

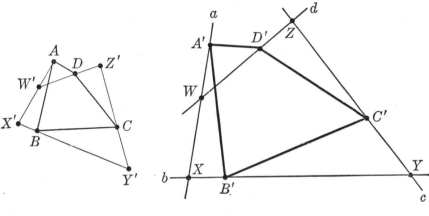

FIG. 107

intersect at Y, c and d intersect at Z, and d and a intersect at W. We wish to locate A' on a, B' on b, C' on c, and D' on d so that quadrilaterals $A'B'C'D'$ and $ABCD$ are directly similar.

Let us use the solution of Problem 1 of § 10.2 to construct a quadrilateral $W'X'Y'Z'$, similar to $WXYZ$, with A on $W'X'$, B on $X'Y'$, C on $Y'Z'$, and D on $Z'W'$. Now locate A' on WX so that A' divides the directed segment WX in the same ratio that A divides the directed segment $W'X'$. To complete the solution, locate B', C', and D' so that they divide XY, YZ, and ZW in the same ratios in which B, C, and D divide $X'Y'$, $Y'Z'$, and $Z'W'$.

Although it is of fundamental importance to seek generalizations, many applications of mathematics use special cases of specific results. We shall consider some special cases of the material of this chapter by letting the given quadrilaterals become triangles.

Problem 2. *Given three points and a triangle, construct lines through the points so that they form a triangle congruent to the given one.*

Solution: In Figure 108, let XYZ be a given triangle and let A, B, and C be given points. We wish to construct a triangle $X'Y'Z'$, congruent to XYZ, with A on $X'Y'$, B on $Y'Z'$, and C on $Z'X'$. Let us consider this as a special case of Problem 1 of § 10.2 by choosing the fourth side d of the given quadrilateral to be the line through Z parallel to XY.

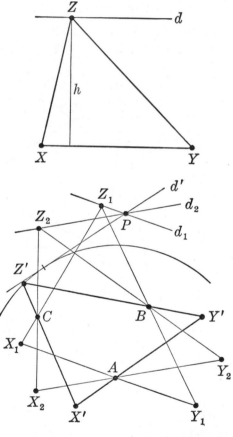

FIG. 108

Draw an arbitrary line through A and locate X_1 and Y_1 on this line so that $\angle CX_1A = \angle ZXY$ and $\angle AY_1B = \angle XYZ$. Let X_1C and Y_1B intersect at Z_1. Let d_1 be the line through Z_1 parallel to X_1Y_1. Likewise construct triangle $X_2Y_2Z_2$, similar to XYZ, with sides passing through

A, B, and C. Let d_2 be the line through Z_2, parallel to X_2Y_2, and let P be the point of intersection of lines d_1 and d_2.

Drop a perpendicular from Z to XY and call this altitude h. Describe the circle with A as center and h as radius. Let d' be a line through P tangent to this circle. Now construct the line through A which is parallel to d' and locate X' and Y' on this line so that $\angle CX'A = \angle ZXY$ and $\angle AY'B = \angle XYZ$. Let $X'C$ and $Y'B$ intersect at Z' to form a triangle similar to XYZ. By the second solution of Problem 1 of § 10.2, it follows that Z' falls on line d'. Since the similar triangles XYZ and $X'Y'Z'$ have corresponding altitudes equal, they are congruent.

For sides $X'Y'$, $Y'Z'$, and $Z'X'$ passing through A, B, and C, respectively, there are two solutions if P is outside the circle with center A and radius h; there is one solution if P is on this circle; there is no solution if P is inside this circle.

Although Problem 2 was suggested as an application of Problem 1 of § 10.2, we might expect that Problem 2 can be solved by more elementary methods. Note that, in Figure 108, points X_1, X_2, and X' lie on the circle through points C and A in which angle ZXY can be inscribed. Since circular loci for vertices Y' and Z' are also easily found, Problem 2 can be solved if a solution for Problem 3, considered below, is known. (If an elementary solution of Problem 3 were not known, a solution could be based on Problem 2 by choosing points B and C on circles P and Q in Figure 109.)

Problem 3. *Let two given circles, with centers P and Q intersect at point A. Through A construct a line so that the segment determined on this line by the other intersections with circles P and Q shall have a given length.*

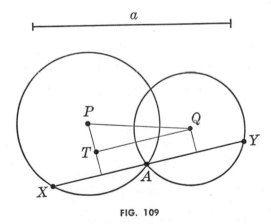

FIG. 109

Analysis: In Figure 109, suppose that chord XY, which passes through A, has the given length a. From P construct a line perpendicular to XY

and from Q construct a line parallel to XY and let these lines intersect at T. Since the perpendicular from the center of a circle to a chord of the circle bisects the chord, it follows that $XY = 2TQ$. Hence if we construct the right triangle with hypotenuse PQ and with side TQ half the length of a, the line through A parallel to TQ will provide one solution. Further details are left for the student.

The discussion in this chapter has been directed toward using known results both to suggest other problems and to form conjectures about possible solution methods. We have not exhausted our subject; each new topic can lead to other related problems. For example, we may extend Problem 2 to ask for the construction of a triangle, congruent to a given one, with each side tangent to a given circle; also, we may conjecture that a solution can be obtained by use of Theorem 1, § 10.3.

Although we have restricted attention to geometry of two dimensions, it should be apparent that many problems of plane geometry have analogies in solid geometry. To extend results of this chapter to three dimensions, we might start with six given points and try to pass planes through each of the points so that the six planes determined a cube. In this case, we might conjecture that if a cube moves so that five of its faces pass through fixed points then the sixth face also passes through a fixed point. If this conjecture were verified, we might expect the problem to have an unlimited number of solutions corresponding to the family of planes through this fixed point and the sixth given point. It is easy to suggest replacing the given points by spheres and substituting another polyhedron for the cube.

If we did provide a detailed discussion for the three space generalization of the material of this chapter, someone might inquire about extending the results to higher dimensions. To attempt this it would be desirable to discuss Problem 1, § 10.1, from the analytic geometry approach. That is, given the co-ordinates of four points we would want to find the equations of lines through the points so that the lines formed a square. For a four-space generalization we could start with eight points, each given by four co-ordinates, and attempt to find equations of "hyper-planes" through these points satisfying proper analytic conditions.

EXERCISES

1. In Figure 109 let the given circles P and Q intersect at A. What is the maximum and minimum lengths of the given segment a for which Problem 3 has solutions?

2. Explain why it is impossible to inscribe a square in a given rectangle, not a square, so that consecutive vertices of the square lie on consecutive sides of the rectangle.

3. Locate one point on each side of a given triangle so that the points are vertices of an equilateral triangle having a given perimeter.

4. Locate one point on each side of a given triangle so that the points

are the vertices of the smallest equilateral triangle that can be inscribed in the given triangle.

5. Inscribe a circle in a given triangle, without bisecting any angle of the triangle.

6. Given five points, not necessarily coplanar, explain a method for constructing a cube with five of its faces passing through these points. (Start with a plane through one point and use the orthogonal projections of the other points on this plane.)

II

Concurrent Lines Associated
with a Triangle

11.1 INTRODUCTION

The Theorem of Ceva, which was introduced in § 2.6, has been used to motivate other work throughout this text; in particular, related material is found in §§ 2.7, 4.3, 8.4, and 8.7. Several times, as in Theorem 2 of § 8.4, we have noted the location of three points, one on each side of a triangle, so that the lines joining these points to the opposite vertices are concurrent and so that the lines perpendicular to the sides of the triangle at these points are also concurrent. The present chapter contains a study of the location of all points on the sides of a triangle which simultaneously satisfy both of these concurrency conditions. Theorem 1, below, is stated to provide a convenient reference for previous notation and results; parts (A), (B), and (C) of Theorem 1 are contained in Theorem 1 of § 2.6, in Theorem 1 of § 4.3, and in Theorem 1 of § 2.5.

Theorem 1. *Let L, M, and N be points on sides BC, CA, and AB of triangle ABC.*

(A) *If* $\dfrac{AN}{NB} \cdot \dfrac{BL}{LC} \cdot \dfrac{CM}{MA} = +1$, *lines AL, BM, and CN are concurrent at a point Q.*

(B) *If* $(BL)^2 + (CM)^2 + (AN)^2 = (LC)^2 + (MA)^2 + (NB)^2$, *the lines perpendicular to BC, CA, and AB at points L, M, and N are concurrent at a point P.*

(C) *If* $\dfrac{AN}{NB} \cdot \dfrac{BL}{LC} \cdot \dfrac{CM}{MA} = -1$, *the points L, M, and N are collinear.*

Consider the special case in which points L and M both coincide with vertex C. If N is any point on AB, the lines AL, BM, and CN are concurrent at C and, furthermore, the points L, M, and N are collinear. In this case we shall say that the set of points (C, C, N) satisfies both part (A) and part (C) of Theorem 1.

In Figure 110, let L be the midpoint, A', of BC and let O be the circumcenter of triangle ABC. Let P be any point on OA' and let M and N be the feet of the perpendiculars from P to CA and to AB. As P recedes toward the ideal point P_∞ on OA', M and N recede toward the ideal points on lines CA and AB. Hence we shall say that the set of points (A', M_∞, N_∞) satisfies part (B) of Theorem 1. The lines AA', BM_∞, and CN_∞ intersect at the point Q for which A' is the midpoint of AQ. Therefore we say that the points (A', M_∞, N_∞) satisfy part (A) of Theorem 1.

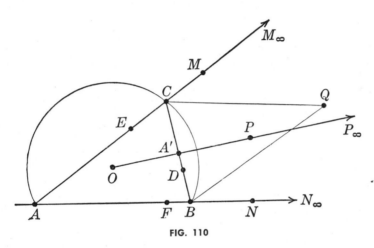

FIG. 110

Are there any points (L, M, N) which satisfy all three parts of Theorem 1 simultaneously? We have noted that points (C, C, N) satisfy parts (A) and (C) for any position of N on AB. If N is the foot of the altitude, perpendiculars to BC, CA, and AB from C, C, and N, respectively, also intersect at point C. Since it is easy to show that parts (A) and (C) of Theorem 1 cannot be satisfied unless the collinear line of part (C) passes through a vertex of the triangle, the only other case we need investigate is that in which the collinear line of part (C) passes through two vertices. For example, let (L, M, N) be the points (B, A, N), where N is an arbitrary point on AB. Then the points B, A, and N are collinear; the lines AL, BM, and CN also intersect at N. To locate N so that part (B) of Theorem 1 is satisfied, construct perpendiculars to CA and BC from A and B. Let these perpendiculars intersect at P and choose N as the foot of the perpendicular from P to AB. We can describe this special location of N by use of the theorem which is proved next.

Theorem 2. *Let L, M, and N be points on sides BC, CA, and AB, respectively, of triangle ABC. Let A', B', and C' be the midpoints of the sides BC, CA, and AB. Let L', M', and N' be the reflections of L, M, and N about points A', B', and C'. Then if points (L, M, N) satisfy any one of the conditions of Theorem 1, the points (L', M', N') satisfy the same condition of Theorem 1.*

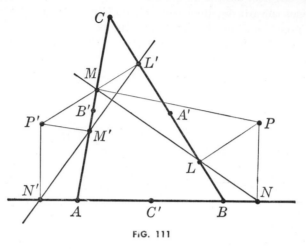

FıG. 111

Proof: In Figure 111 we note that, using directed segments, $BL = L'C$, $LC = BL'$, $CM = M'A$, $MA = CM'$, $AN = N'B$, and $NB = AN'$. After substitution in the three equalities of Theorem 1 and making simple rearrangements, we obtain the original equalities with L replaced by L', M replaced by M', and N replaced by N'.

It follows that if (L, M, N) satisfy two conditions of Theorem 1, (L', M', N') must satisfy both conditions. In Figure 111, both (L, M, N) and (L', M', N') satisfy parts (B) and (C) of Theorem 1. In Figure 112,

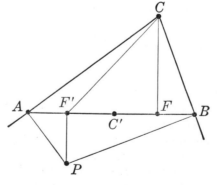

FıG. 112

F is the foot of the altitude from C so that points (C, C, F) satisfy all three conditions of Theorem 1. By reflection of these points about the midpoints of the proper sides we obtain the points (B, A, F') which also satisfy all three parts of Theorem 1.

Theorem 3 describes all sets of points (L, M, N) which simultaneously satisfy all three parts of Theorem 1. Theorem 4 shows the points which satisfy both parts (A) and (C) of Theorem 1. Sets of points which simultaneously satisfy two other parts of Theorem 1 will be considered later.

Theorem 3. *The only points (L, M, N) which simultaneously satisfy all three parts of Theorem 1 are $(D, A, A), (C, C, F), (B, E, B), (D', C, B)$, (B, A, F'), and (C, E', A).*

Theorem 4. *The only points (L, M, N) which simultaneously satisfy parts (A) and (C) of Theorem 1 are $(L, A, A), (C, C, N), (B, M, B)$, $(L, C, B), (B, A, N)$, and (C, M, A).*

In Theorems 3 and 4 L, M, and N represent arbitrary points on sides BC, CA, and AB, respectively, of triangle ABC. Points D, E, and F are the feet of the altitudes from vertices A, B, and C. The points D', E', and F' are the reflections of D, E, and F about the midpoints of the sides on which these points lie.

EXERCISES

1. Using the notation of Theorem 1, the points L, M, and N are collinear if $AN \cdot BL \cdot CM = -NB \cdot LC \cdot MA$. If one of the points L, M, or N coincides with a vertex of triangle ABC, both members of this equality vanish. Show, however, that L, M, and N need not be collinear for this special case.

2. If L, M, and N are feet of the altitudes, parts (A) and (B) of Theorem 1 are satisfied. Theorem 2 gives a second set of points which satisfy parts (A) and (B) of Theorem 1. For both sets of points describe the location of points P and Q, the points of concurrency of Theorem 1.

3. Let P and Q be the points of concurrency described in Theorem 1. For the special set of points contained in Theorem 3, find the locus of P and find the locus of Q.

4. Let Q be the point in which Cevian lines of triangle ABC meet. For the special points contained in Theorem 4, describe the locus of Q.

11.2   THE SIMSON LINE

We now consider sets of points (L, M, N) which simultaneously satisfy parts (B) and (C) of Theorem 1 of § 11.1; not only must L, M, and N

be collinear but lines perpendicular to the sides of the triangle at these points must meet in a common point P. The following analysis employs standard methods of analytic geometry to obtain the equation of the locus of P.

Given a triangle ABC, in Figure 113, we choose a rectangular co-ordinate system so that the vertices have co-ordinates $A(-1,0)$, $B(1,0)$, and $C(d,e)$. Let $P(x,y)$ be any point in the plane and let perpendiculars

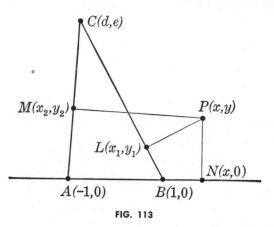

FIG. 113

from P to BC, CA, and AB cut these lines at points $L(x_1,y_1)$, $M(x_2,y_2)$, and $N(x,0)$. Direct computation of the co-ordinates of L and M in terms of the co-ordinates of C and P gives the following results.

$$x_1 = \frac{x + d^2x + dey - 2dx - ey + e^2}{e^2 + d^2 - 2d + 1}$$

$$y_1 = \frac{dex + e^2y + e - ex - de}{e^2 + d^2 - 2d + 1}$$

$$x_2 = \frac{x + d^2x + dey + 2dx + ey - e^2}{e^2 + d^2 + 2d + 1}$$

$$y_2 = \frac{dex + e^2y + e + ex + de}{e^2 + d^2 + 2d + 1}$$

The condition that L, M, and N be collinear requires that the determinant

$$\begin{vmatrix} x_1 & y_1 & 1 \\ x_2 & y_2 & 1 \\ x & 0 & 1 \end{vmatrix}$$

be equal to zero. Use of elementary properties of determinants will simplify the computations which show that L, M, and N are collinear only if

$$e(x^2 + y^2) + (1 - d^2 - e^2)y - e = 0.$$

Since this is the equation of the circle passing through each vertex of triangle ABC, we have completed an analytic geometry proof of Theorem 4 of § 2.4. The line through L, M, and N is the Simson Line of the point P on the circumcircle.

Problem 1. *Given point L on side BC of triangle ABC, locate points M and N, on sides CA and AB, so parts (B) and (C) of Theorem 1 of § 11.1 are satisfied.*

Solution: At L erect a line perpendicular to BC and let this line cut the circumcircle of ABC at P. Drop perpendiculars to CA and AB from P to locate M and N. There may be two, one, or no solutions.

EXERCISES

1. Supply the missing steps in finding the co-ordinates of point M, Figure 113, in terms of x, y, d, and e.

2. The proof of Theorem 4, § 2.4, is more elegant than the proof given in this section. Does the analytic geometry method have any advantages over the earlier method?

3. Supply details in finding the equation of the locus of P, Figure 113, if L, M, and N are collinear. Assume that co-ordinates of L, M, and N are already expressed in terms of x, y, d, and e.

4. List specific points on the sides of a triangle, such as midpoints of the sides, which satisfy both parts (A) and (B) of Theorem 1 of § 11.1.

11.3 RELATED POINTS OF CONCURRENCY

If the points (L, M, N) simultaneously satisfy parts (A) and (B) of Theorem 1 of § 11.1, not only must lines joining L, M, and N to the opposite vertices meet in a point Q but lines perpendicular to the sides of the triangle at these points must meet in a common point P. At numerous places in this text specific points which satisfy both of these conditions have been mentioned; Table 1 contains twenty sets of these points.

In Table 1, A', B', and C' are midpoints of sides; D, E, and F are feet of altitudes; D', E', and F' are reflections of D, E, and F about A', B', and C'; X, Y, and Z, without subscripts are points of contact of the inscribed circle and with subscripts, are points of contact of ex-circles; L_∞, M_∞, and N_∞ are ideal points on BC, CA, and AB.

Each position of P shown in Table 1 is the Miquel point (§ 8.8) of the associated points on the triangle ABC. For each set of points in

TABLE 1

SETS OF POINTS WHICH SATISFY
PARTS (A) AND (B) OF THEOREM 1 OF § 11.1

Set No.	Location of (L,M,N)	Position of P	Position of Q
1	(A',B',C')	O	G
2	(D,E,F)	H	H
3	(D',E',F')	H^*	H''
4	(X,Y,Z)	I	Q_4
5	(X_1,Y_2,Z_3)	I^*	Q_4''
6	(X_1,Y_1,Z_1)	I_1	Q_5
7	(X,Y_3,Z_2)	I_1^*	Q_5''
8	(X_2,Y_2,Z_2)	I_2	Q_6
9	(X_3,Y,Z_1)	I_2^*	Q_6''
10	(X_3,Y_3,Z_3)	I_3	Q_7
11	(X_2,Y_1,Z)	I_3^*	Q_7''
12	(D,A,A)	A	A
13	(D',C,B)	A^*	A''
14	(B,E,B)	B	B
15	(C,E',A)	B^*	B''
16	(C,C,F)	C	C
17	(B,A,F')	C^*	C''
18	(A',M_∞,N_∞)	P_1	Q_1
19	(L_∞,B',N_∞)	P_2	Q_2
20	(L_∞,M_∞,C')	P_3	Q_3

Table 1, Theorem 2 of § 11.1 may be used to find a related set of points satisfying the desired conditions; for sets 1, 18, 19, and 20 the same set is obtained. It is easy to show that for two sets so related, sets 4 and 5 for example, the two positions of P determine a line segment which is bisected by the circumcenter O. Also, for such sets, the two positions of Q are isotomic conjugate points (§ 8.7).

In listing positions of P: H is the orthocenter; I is the incenter; I_1, I_2, and I_3 are excenters; P_1, P_2, and P_3 are ideal points on the perpendicular bisectors of sides BC, CA, and AB. Asterisks are used to designate the reflection of a point about O, the circumcenter. In set 13, for example, perpendiculars to the sides of ABC at D', C, and B intersect at A^* where O is the midpoint of segment A^*A.

In listing positions of Q, Q'' denotes the isotomic conjugate of Q: G is the centroid; Q_4 is the Gergonne point and Q_4'' is the Nagel point (§ 8.7); A'', B'', and C'' coincide with points D', E', and F'; points Q_1, Q_2, and Q_3 are reflections of A, B, and C about points A', B', and C'.

For each set of points in Table 1, the student should verify that the Cevian lines are concurrent and that the perpendiculars to the sides are concurrent. For sets 1 and 2, these properties are well known in elementary geometry; for sets 3 through 11, proofs can be made by the methods of § 8.4; for sets 13 through 20, proofs can be based on the discussion of § 11.1.

We now consider a method for finding additional sets of points which simultaneously satisfy parts (A) and (B) of Theorem 1 of § 11.1. In Figure 114, let L_1, M_1, and N_1 be points on BC, CA, and AB so that lines perpendicular to the sides of triangle ABC at these points are concurrent at P_1. Construct the circle, with center S, which passes through points L_1, M_1, and N_1 and let this circle again cut the sides of the triangle in points L_2, M_2, and N_2. Note that the perpendicular bisectors

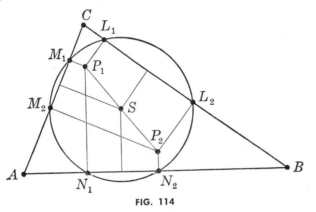

FIG. 114

of chords L_1L_2, M_1M_2, and N_1N_2 are concurrent at S. It follows that the line perpendicular to BC at L_2 cuts P_1S at point P_2 where $P_1S = SP_2$. Since perpendiculars to the sides at M_2 and N_2 must also pass through P_2, the points (L_2, M_2, N_2) satisfy part (B) of Theorem 1, § 11.1.

Now assume that, in Figure 114, the Cevian lines AL_1, BM_1, and CN_1 are concurrent. Are the lines AL_2, BM_2, and CN_2 also concurrent? Let

$$\frac{AN_1}{N_1B} \cdot \frac{BL_1}{L_1C} \cdot \frac{CM_1}{M_1A} = 1.$$

Using directed segments in Theorem 2 of § 2.2 we have

$$AN_1 \cdot AN_2 = AM_1 \cdot AM_2,$$
$$BL_1 \cdot BL_2 = BN_1 \cdot BN_2,$$
$$CM_1 \cdot CM_2 = CL_1 \cdot CL_2.$$

Hence $\dfrac{AN_1}{M_1A} = \dfrac{AM_2}{N_2A}$, $\dfrac{BL_1}{N_1B} = \dfrac{BN_2}{L_2B}$,   and $\dfrac{CM_1}{L_1C} = \dfrac{CL_2}{M_2C}$.

Since the product of the left members of these equalities is 1, the product of the right members may be rearranged to give

$$\frac{AN_2}{N_2B} \cdot \frac{BL_2}{L_2C} \cdot \frac{CM_2}{M_2A} = 1.$$

This shows that the Cevian lines L_2, M_2, and N_2 are concurrent. Results of the above discussion are summarized in Theorem 1.

Theorem 1. *Let the points* (L_1, M_1, N_1) *satisfy parts* (A) *and* (B) *of Theorem 1 of § 11.1. Let the circle through* L_1, M_1, *and* N_1 *cut sides* BC, CA, *and* AB *in new points* L_2, M_2, *and* N_2. *Then the points* (L_2, M_2, N_2) *also satisfy parts* (A) *and* (B) *of Theorem 1 of § 11.1.*

Not only does Theorem 1 tell how to find additional points satisfying parts (A) and (B) of Theorem 1 of § 11.1 but when combined with Theorem 2 of § 11.1 it may be used to produce many such points when one set of points satisfying both conditions is known. For example, let us start with the midpoints of the sides, set 1 in Table 1, and construct a circle through them (the nine-point circle in this case) to locate three new points, in this case we obtain set 2 in Table 1. Then we reflect these points about the midpoints of the sides, this gives set 3 in Table 1. If we now pass a circle through D', E', and F', we obtain a fourth set of points satisfying both desired conditions and this set does not coincide with any set in Table 1, for a general triangle. To find a fifth set we reflect the points of the fourth set about the midpoints of the sides. We make no attempt to determine whether continuation of this process will give an unlimited number of distinct sets or if the same points will repeat periodically.

EXERCISES

1. For set 18 in Table 1, prove that ABQ_1C is a parallelogram.
2. For each set of points in Table 1, tell whether or not Theorem 1 can be used to produce a new set which is not in Table 1. When two points coincide, as in set 12, can Theorem 1 be modified to produce new points satisfying parts (A) and (B) of Theorem 1 of § 11.1?
3. In triangle ABC let $BC = CA$ and let C' be the midpoint of AB. Pick P as any point on $C'C$ and let perpendiculars from P to BC, CA, and AB cut these sides in points L, M, and N. Show that the points (L, M, N) satisfy both parts (A) and (B) of Theorem 1 of § 11.1. As P moves along $C'C$, what is the locus of point Q, the intersection of the Cevian lines?

11.4 A CUBIC CURVE

Finally we consider finding the locus of the point P associated with points (L, M, N) for which parts (A) and (B) of Theorem 1 of § 11.1 are satisfied simultaneously. The twenty locations of P shown in Table 1 of § 11.3 suggest that the locus is not composed of straight lines and circles. Indeed, if the locus is a continuous curve, sets 18, 19, and 20 of Table 1 indicate that the three perpendicular bisectors of the sides of the triangle are asymptotes of this curve.

We again apply analytic geometry methods and adopt the notation used in § 11.2 and in Figure 113. For the triangle shown in Figure 113 we have already computed the co-ordinates of L, M, and N in terms of x, y, d, and e. We now write equations of lines AL, BM, and CN and impose the condition that these lines be concurrent at a point Q. The details of this computation are omitted; they are tedious even with use of a determinant form for the condition that three lines be concurrent. The computation gives the following equation for the locus of P.

$$(d^2 - 1)x^3 + (2de)x^2y + (e^2)xy^2 + (d - d^3 - de^2)x^2 +$$
$$(e - e^3 - d^2e)xy + (1 - d^2)x - (2de)y + (d^3 + de^2 - d) = 0$$

From Theorem 2 of § 11.1, it follows that this locus is symmetric about the circumcenter of triangle ABC. In Figure 113, the circumcenter is at the point

$$x = 0, \quad y = \frac{e^2 + d^2 - 1}{2e}.$$

When the origin is translated to this point, the equation of the locus assumes the following form.

$$(d^2 - 1)x^3 + 2dex^2y + e^2xy^2 - 2dey +$$
$$\tfrac{1}{4}(3 - d^4 - e^4 - 2d^2e^2 + 2e^2 - 2d^2)x = 0$$

If $d = 0$, so that triangle ABC is isosceles, this equation becomes

$$x\left(x^2 - e^2y^2 + \frac{e^4 - 2e^2 - 3}{4}\right) = 0.$$

In this case, the locus of P consists of the perpendicular bisector of the base and a hyperbola for which the perpendicular bisectors of the equal sides are asymptotes.

If $e = \sqrt{3}$ and $d = 0$, the triangle is equilateral and the locus of P has the equation

$$x(x + \sqrt{3}y)(x - \sqrt{3}y) = 0$$

so that the entire locus consists of the perpendicular bisectors of the three sides.

In general, nine points are sufficient to completely determine a cubic curve of the form

$$ax^3 + bx^2y + cxy^2 + dy^3 + ex^2 + fxy + gy^2 + hx + iy + j = 0.$$

It is, therefore, of interest to find a cubic curve which passes through ten or more given points. The co-ordinates of point C, in Figure 113, can be chosen so that triangle ABC is directly similar to any given triangle, say XYZ. If these similar triangles are in the same plane, ABC may be made to coincide with XYZ by a rotation, a translation, and a change of scale. In each of these transformations the equation of the locus of P is changed into another cubic equation. We may, therefore, state the following theorem.

Theorem 1. *The first seventeen values of P, in Table 1 of § 11.3, lie on the same cubic curve; from any point on this curve perpendiculars to the sides of triangle ABC determine three points which satisfy Ceva's Theorem; the perpendicular bisectors of the sides of the triangle are asymptotes of this curve.*

If triangle ABC is isosceles but not equilateral, part of the cubic locus of Theorem 1 is a hyperbola. The asymptotes and a point on a hyperbola determine a hyperbola uniquely. The information in Table 1 enables us to state a theorem about the particular hyperbola associated with an isosceles triangle.

Theorem 2. *The hyperbola which passes through one base vertex of an isosceles triangle and has the perpendicular bisectors of the equal sides as asymptotes also passes through the second base vertex and through two excenters of the triangle.*

For each point on the locus of P, so that parts (A) and (B) of Theorem 1 of § 11.1 are satisfied, we can construct a corresponding point on the locus of Q, the intersection of the Cevian lines. We need only drop perpendiculars to two sides and connect the feet of these segments to the opposite vertices. We shall use this method to find the equation of the locus of Q for a very special triangle.

Problem 1. *Let the triangle ABC have co-ordinates $A(-1,-1)$, $B(1,-1)$, and $C(-1,1)$. Find the equation of the locus of point Q so that parts (A) and (B) of Theorem 1 of § 11.1 are satisfied simultaneously.*

Solution: By the formulas of this section it is easy to find that the locus of P consists of the straight line $y = x$ and the hyperbola $xy = -1$.

Assume that, in Figure 115, $P(x,y)$ is a point on the locus of P and that $Q(u,v)$ is the corresponding point on the locus of Q. The co-ordinates of M and N, obtained by dropping perpendiculars from P, are $M(-1,y)$ and $N(x,-1)$. We now write the equations of BQ and CQ and solve for the intersections of these lines with CA and AB to find the co-ordinates of M and N in terms of u and v. These points are

$$M\left(-1, \frac{u + 2v + 1}{1 - u}\right) \quad \text{and} \quad N\left(\frac{v + 2u + 1}{1 - v}, -1\right).$$

Hence, to find the equation of the locus of Q, we replace x and y in the equation of the locus of P by the relations

$$x = \frac{v + 2u + 1}{1 - v} \quad \text{and} \quad y = \frac{u + 2v + 1}{1 - u}.$$

In this transformation, the equation $y = x$ becomes $v = u$, and the hyperbola $xy = -1$ becomes another hyperbola

$$u^2 + v^2 + 3uv + u + v + 1 = 0.$$

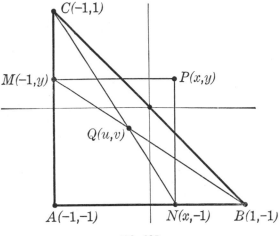

FIG. 115

EXERCISES

1. Let L be a fixed point on side BC of triangle ABC. In how many points can the perpendicular to BC at L cut the cubic locus for point P?

2. Carry out the details in the solution of Problem 1.

3. For a general triangle, sketch the locus of point P so that parts (A) and (B) of Theorem 1 of § 11.1 are satisfied. Sketch the locus for P for two isosceles triangles; in one let the equal sides be longer than the third side, in the other let the third side be longer.

4. A hyperbola is the locus of points the difference of whose distances from two fixed points is constant. Explain how this property may be used to locate points on a hyperbola using ruler and compass.

5. Find the center and asymptotes of the hyperbola

$$u^2 + v^2 + 3uv + u + v + 1 = 0.$$

6. Theorem 2 relates a hyperbola to an isosceles triangle. Given a hyperbola, can an isosceles triangle be determined so the triangle and

the hyperbola satisfy the conditions of Theorem 2? If a solution is possible, is the solution unique?

7. Does the transformation

$$x = \frac{v + 2u + 1}{1 - v}, \quad y = \frac{u + 2v + 1}{1 - u}$$

change every conic section into a conic section?

12

Impossible Ruler and Compass Constructions

~~~~~~

12.1 INTRODUCTION

The problem of attempting to trisect an angle using an unmarked ruler and compass is of considerable popular interest. After a geometry teacher says the problem cannot be solved, he may find a student who spends considerable time in trying to invent a construction method. A competent mathematics teacher should be able to discuss impossible constructions, to provide references to proofs that certain constructions are impossible, and to explain why these proofs are not contained in an elementary geometry text.

Some persons refuse to believe that any problem cannot be solved. Numerous amateurs mail incorrect constructions and proofs to college mathematics professors. Occasionally a professor will receive elaborate plans for a perpetual motion machine; the "inventor" may even request a donation to help construct a working model. Sometimes a person prints and distributes a book which, he claims, shows that mathematicians are wrong when they say that certain problems have no solutions. It is unfortunate that such persons lack either the ability or the interest to study rigorous mathematical proofs.

It is easy to propose a construction problem which has no solution; no one can construct a straight line through each vertex of an equilateral triangle. Other problems have exact solutions which cannot be constructed by ruler and compass. An ellipse is the locus of points the sum of whose distances from two fixed points is a constant. The ellipse cannot be fully drawn by ruler and compass; theoretically we can construct an exact ellipse using two pins, a loop of string, and a tracing point.

Three famous problems which were considered by ancient Greek geometers are trisecting an angle, doubling a cube, and squaring a circle. After no valid solutions were produced in 2000 years, it was finally proved that they could not be solved by ruler and compass methods. To **trisect an angle** one must provide an exact geometrical construction, using only ruler and compass, which will divide any given angle into three equal angles. To **double a cube** we must construct a line segment so that a cube with this segment as an edge will have twice the volume of a given cube. To **square a circle** means to construct a square whose area is equal to the area of a given circle.

Some persons who persist in trying to solve these problems fail to realize that these problems are theoretical instead of practical. When we say that a construction is exact, we are assuming that the ruler and compass are perfectly precise and that each step of the construction can be carried out with absolutely no error.

12.2   CRITERION OF CONSTRUCTIBILITY

We cannot prove that certain constructions are impossible if we use only methods of synthetic geometry. The proofs depend upon a type of mathematical analysis usually found in a course in theory of equations. For this reason, results are stated here without proof; an interested reader may consult Dickson* or Courant and Robbins.†

We often change a construction problem into an equivalent problem involving algebraic analysis. In Chapter 1 we found real roots of linear and quadratic equations using ruler and compass. For example, the cubic equation

$$x^3 + 3x^2 - 2x - 6 = 0$$

has one rational root, $x = -3$, and two irrational roots, $x = +\sqrt{2}$ and $x = -\sqrt{2}$. Starting with a unit segment, we can construct a directed line segment equal to any one of these roots. We solve the related equations $x + 3 = 0$ and $x^2 - 2 = 0$.

For showing that some constructions are impossible, the important result is that *a construction problem cannot be solved by ruler and compass if the corresponding algebraic problem cannot be reduced to the solution of linear and quadratic equations.* As a special case of this criterion, we state the following theorem without proof.

Theorem 1. *If a cubic equation with integers as coefficients, has no rational root, then none of its roots can be constructed with ruler and compass.*

* Leonard E. Dickson, *First Course in the Theory of Equations* (John Wiley, 1922), pp. 29–44.

† Richard Courant and Herbert Robbins, *What Is Mathematics?* (Oxford, 1941), pp. 127–140.

We may apply Theorem 1 to show that the problem of doubling a cube cannot be solved by ruler and compass. If the edge of a given cube has length x, a cube with twice the volume of the given one must have an edge of length $\sqrt[3]{2}x$. Since the cube root of 2 is one root of the cubic equation $y^3 - 2 = 0$, which has no rational root, the construction cannot be made with ruler and compass.

To square a circle whose radius is r, we must construct a line segment having the length $\sqrt{\pi}r$. This can be done if and only if we can construct a line segment of length π, starting with a unit segment. By definition, a *transcendental number* is a number that is not a root of any polynomial equation with integral coefficients. By the criterion of this section, no transcendental number is constructible. It has been proved, using advanced analysis which is normally postponed until graduate work, that π is a transcendental number.

12.3 ANGLE TRISECTION

To prove that a general angle cannot be trisected with ruler and compass, it is sufficient to show that one particular angle cannot be trisected. Using the criterion of § 12.2, we shall show that an angle of 60° cannot be trisected.

An angle of 60° can be trisected if and only if we can construct an angle of 20°. Starting with a unit segment, we can construct an angle of 20° if and only if we can construct a segment of length x so that $x = \cos 20°$. From elementary trigonometry we use the identity

$$\cos A = 4 \cos^3 \frac{A}{3} - 3 \cos \frac{A}{3}.$$

If we replace A by 60°, we obtain

$$\tfrac{1}{2} = 4 \cos^3 20° - 3 \cos 20°$$

or

$$8x^3 - 6x - 1 = 0.$$

Since this cubic equation has no rational root, Theorem 1 of § 12.2 shows that an angle of 20° is not constructible by ruler and compass.

The above results also show that it is impossible to construct a regular polygon of nine sides, since a side of this polygon would subtend an angle of 40° at the center of the circumscribed circle. In § 3.3 it was noted that an angle of 3° can be constructed. By repeated additions we may construct angles of 18° and of 21°. Since an angle of 20° is not constructible, angles of 1° and of 2° cannot be constructed. If k is a positive integer, it follows that an angle of k degrees is constructible if and only if k is a multiple of 3.

It is possible to trisect any angle exactly if we are permitted to use instruments other than an unmarked ruler and compass. As an illustration, let us suppose that we may use a straightedge which contains two marked points. Denote these positions by L and M and let the distance between L and M be r. Also, let us assume that we may place the straightedge so that L lies on a given line and M lies on the circumference of a given circle, as we can do if the line and the circle are not too far apart.

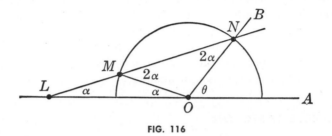

FIG. 116

In Figure 116, let $\angle AOB$ be given. With O as center and r as radius, describe a circle cutting OB at point N. Adjust the marked straightedge so that M falls on circle O, L falls on line OA, and line LM passes through N. Designate $\angle AOB$ by θ and $\angle ALB$ by α. We shall prove that $\alpha = \dfrac{\theta}{3}$ so that angle θ has been trisected.

Since $LM = MO = r$, $\angle MOL = \alpha$. Using triangle LOM, exterior angle $NMO = 2\alpha$ and since $MO = NO$, $\angle MNO = 2\alpha$. In triangle NOM it follows that $\angle NOM = 180° - 4\alpha$. From the three angles into which straight angle AOL is divided, we have

$$180° = \theta + 180° - 4\alpha + \alpha.$$

Simplification gives the desired result

$$\alpha = \frac{\theta}{3}.$$

For practical applications, an approximate solution may be satisfactory. Most persons would use a protractor if required to trisect an angle approximately. If we use only ruler and compass, we can construct an angle which is approximately one-third the size of a given angle.

For a practical approximate solution it is often desirable to find a first approximation, then to find a better second approximation, then to find a still better third approximation, and to continue until the final approximation contains an error smaller than a specified amount.

To trisect angle AOB approximately (see Figure 117) we may adjust a compass so that arc AC is smaller than one-third of arc AB. By constructing the equal arcs AC, CD, and DE we have

$$\tfrac{1}{3}\angle AOB = \angle DOE + \tfrac{1}{3}\angle EOB.$$

If we now adjust the compass so that it intercepts an arc smaller than one-third of arc EB, we may approximate one-third of angle EOB. By continuing this process, we can obtain one-third of angle AOB as the sum of known angles plus an unknown angle which is arbitrarily small.

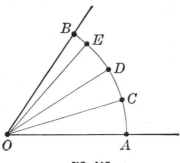

FIG. 117

Old copies of *The American Mathematical Monthly* provide a fruitful source for articles and problems concerning geometrical constructions. A topical index for this magazine will show that about twenty articles concerned with the trisection problem have appeared in the last fifty years.

INDEX